The Medicinal Herb Grower

A Guide for Cultivating Plants that Heal

Volume 1

Disclaimer

Although all cultures on earth use plant-derived medicaments, we cannot recommend self medication with plant products. Rather we offer medicinal information in the context of historical usage and from personal experieince, augmented by our studies of current research. Please seek the care and advice of a qualified healthcare practitioner for all medical problems. We do not accept responsibility for the use or misuse of any of the herbal information found in this book, or for any accident or injury caused by growing, handling or ingesting plants, or from attempting to follow processes described in this book.

—Richard A. "Richo" Cech and Horizon Herbs LLC

Book orders may be directed to:

Horizon Herbs LLC
PO Box 69
Williams, OR 97544-0069
USA

phone: (541) 846-6704

fax: (541) 846-6233

http://www.horizonherbs.com

The Medicinal Herb Grower Volume 1

Published by Horizon Herbs LLC

10 9 8 7 6 5 4 3 2 1
ISBN 0-9700312-2-X

The Medicinal Herb Grower

A Guide for Cultivating Plants that Heal

Volume 1

by Richo Cech
illustrated by Sena Cech

A Horizon Herbs Publication
Williams, Oregon
2009

By the Same Author

Horizon Herbs Seed Catalog

Published twice yearly, this catalog provides access to organically grown live roots, plants, and open-pollinated seeds of over 800 species of medicinal plants from all over the world. FREE

Making Plant Medicine

Originally published in the year 2000, "Making Plant Medicine" has become a preferred herbal reference, used by medicine makers of all descriptions, having found its way into kitchens, herbal laboratories, and herb schools across the continent and abroad. The book provides step-by-step instructions on how to make simple tinctures, vinegar extracts, glycerites, syrups, teas, decoctions, herb infused oils, salves, poultices, compresses, and soaks. You can make professional quality herbal tinctures from a wide range of medicinal herbs that can easily be grown in the home garden. The extensive formulary includes 116 herbs—parts used, practical uses, dosages, contraindications, and hundreds of specific formulas.

ISBN 0-9700312-0-3, 277 pages, soft cover.

Growing At-Risk Medicinal Herbs

"This book is far more than it seems. Don't underestimate what Richo has accomplished. He has taken some of the most difficult plants imaginable, plants that sometimes find even the breath of humans to be anathema, and figured out what they need in order to grow near us and by our leave. He has a good brain and dirty fingernails." —from the foreword by Michael Moore

ISBN 0-9700312-1-1, 282 pages, soft cover.

Book orders may be directed to:

Horizon Herbs LLC
PO Box 69
Williams, OR 97544-0069
USA

phone: (541) 846-6704

fax: (541) 846-6233

http://www.horizonherbs.com

This book is dedicated to all gardeners, everywhere.

Acknowledgements

Thanks to my entire family for supporting and encouraging me to bring this work to completion. Sena, thank you for your love, your dedication, and your boundless creativity. You make mice out of men and men out of mice. Mayche, thank you for your love, your careful editing, and your layout. One does not normally like to sleep with one's editor, but in a garden of medicinal herbs, anything is possible.

Thanks to my friends at Horizon Herbs who keep the vision strong and real. Thanks to everyone who gardens. Thanks to those of you who supported the creation of "The Medicinal Herb Grower" by purchasing it before it was ready. Your faith is right here in this book, and you own this book not so much because you bought it with money, but because you believed in it—and that's a better kind of ownership. May this book help you spread the blessing of healing herbs far and wide.

This book is dedicated to all gardeners, everywhere.

Acknowledgements

Thanks to my entire family for supporting and encouraging me to bring this work to completion. Sena, thank you for your love, your dedication, and your boundless creativity. You make mice out of men and men out of mice. Mayche, thank you for your love, your careful editing, and your layout. One does not normally like to sleep with one's editor, but in a garden of medicinal herbs, anything is possible.

Thanks to my friends at Horizon Herbs who keep the vision strong and real. Thanks to everyone who gardens. Thanks to those of you who supported the creation of "The Medicinal Herb Grower" by purchasing it before it was ready. Your faith is right here in this book, and you own this book not so much because you bought it with money, but because you believed in it—and that's a better kind of ownership. May this book help you spread the blessing of healing herbs far and wide.

The Medicinal Herb Grower
A Guide for Cultivating Plants that Heal
Volume 1

Table of Contents

Addendums

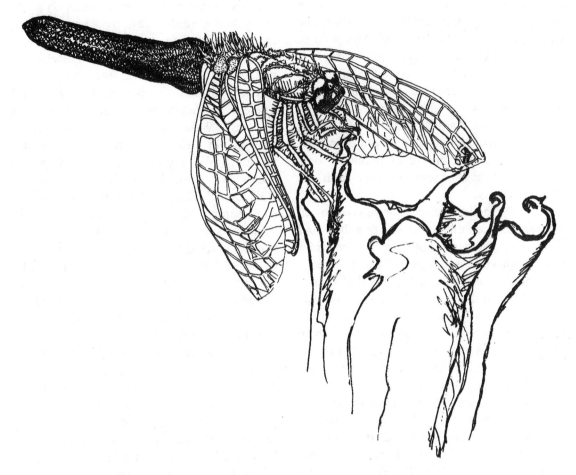

THE TALE OF THE GOLDEN DRAGONFLY

The door of the greenhouse is wide open, allowing the gentle zephyrs of summer to circulate among myriads of medicinal plants. Low stone walls curve out from the doorway, defining flowerbeds filled with rich layers of compost, loam, and sand. In the bed to the right grows a trumpet vine creeper, trellised up against the greenhouse, its clusters of orange blossoms heralding in the solstice. In the bed to the left grows a datura, its hairy purple-green stem and lance-shaped leaves crowned by a single flower, bolt upright, partly unfurled, and ready to flare.

Near the apex of this flower rests a magnificent dragonfly, the likes of which I've never seen. Its thorax is red-gold and textured like the finest velvet, made up of shimmering,

flattened segments. Its wings are nearly transparent (as I can see the purple veins of the datura flower right through them), yet they are undeniably present, a fine-wrought filigree of pure gold.

The sturdy legs of the dragonfly shift a little and the thorax expands and contracts as if with a deep sigh. The globose head faces me now, and the dragonfly fixes me with its all-knowing, deep green eyes. Then, it reaches up with its two front legs, grabs itself by the sides of the head and, still engaging me with its stare, rotates its head exactly upside-down!

But I get ahead of myself here. Before this could all happen (the greenhouse, the rock walls, the datura, and the dragonfly) other things had to occur. It all started back at

1

Horizon School. We lived in a one-room wooden yurt in the middle of a vegetable garden, at the base of Grayback Mountain in the Southern Oregon Siskiyou Mountains.

For five years, we were the caretakers of this alternative school, a loose-knit group of parental misfits and their progeny (children with names like Stardust, Meadowlark, River, and Tarragon), with no binding philosophy of education except a dislike of public schools and a shared sense of respect for the earth and all its creatures.

The facility (besides our yurt) consisted of a ramshackle farm house with preschool and community kitchen, another yurt (the older kids' classroom), a playground that featured a very precarious slide, and a two-holed out-house down in the woods. The farmhouse was permeable to skunks, and it was not at all uncommon to have one waddling through in the early morning, looking for a snack, I guess. None of us wanted to confront a skunk (the untouchable of the animal kingdom), so to keep the peace, we just let it do its thing.

We built the older kids' classroom entirely of rough-cut pine boards (the cheapest wood then available), which had one main drawback—in the hot sun, the roof (which was also the ceiling) leaked copious quantities of pine pitch onto objects below, including books, desks, children's heads, and a continuous parade of teachers. At first, the teachers thought they could work for peanuts in these conditions, but somewhere along the line decided that actually they could not, which is why there was such a procession of them. The only advantage of the pine pitch was its poten-tial as a prophylactic against head lice!

The outhouse overlooked the wood-lands and a boggy lowland pasture where white trilliums grew in profusion. Once, when my wife, Mayche, and I attended a conference on bioregionalism, the group leader asked us to envision ourselves in a place of solitude and peace. We both immediately flashed on the outhouse and our daily visits where, on a nor-mally hectic school day, we spent our only moments of respite.

Mayche was the preschool teacher and mother to all, and I was the earth science teacher, grounds keeper, and "Mr. Fixit." There were inevitable morning circles where we sang, "Wake up, wake up, the rooster has crowed" or "Happiness runs in a circular motion." We regularly performed puppet shows that depicted the Horizon School as "OK Land." The puppets were dressed in left-over scraps of fabric, sometimes homely, sometimes fantastically colorful. Actually, this was not much different from the clothing worn by the students themselves. For the most part, the songs and puppet shows accurately por-trayed what it was like for a child to attend our school. The rooster did crow, everybody ran around in circles, and it was all OK!

School meetings, however, with parents present and kids all tucked in bed, were a different story. Suddenly "OK Land" turned into "Not OK Land." The lack of binding philosophy left parents and teachers adrift in a sea of confused desires and expectations. Despite all this, at the height of its glory, the school harbored 45 children away from public school. And, our children grew up in the gar-den and the woods, living a life full of nature, freedom, and love.

Looking back, I can see our kids the way they were. Jeb loved to dress Sena in cos-tumes of his own making, and she yielded patiently to all his attentions. This time Sena was a duck. The effect was unmistakable. In a stroke of genius, my son had taken his mom's sewing bag, which had flattened wooden han-dles, emptied out half the contents (into the middle of the floor of the yurt, of course), and had Sena wear it like a backpack, threading her thin arms through the handles, with one bloat-ed corner of the bag sticking out behind.

Magically, this was no longer a sewing bag, but a fat duck body swinging behind with wing-like protuberances (the handles of the bag) poking out in front. He fashioned a bill

out of yellow construction paper and rubber-banded it around her platinum blonde hair. At this time, she had a row of spontaneous dread-locks hanging down behind, which I hope was more of a sign of freedom and less a sign of neglect. She wore a pair of faded red pants.

Jeb finished out the costume with yellow construction paper duck feet that he permanently hot-glue-gunned to her only pair of sneakers. All Sena had to do was swing her rear end around and go "Quack!" Despite the fact that the sewing kit was now largely inac-cessible, we were all in stitches.

Another day, I was out milking the goats and happened to look over to see the rear end of Jeb exiting from the only openable win-dow of the older kid's classroom. The soles of his bare feet flashed in the sun as he kicked up his heels and ran into the woods.

Soon, the merry staccato of hammer-ing reverberated from the direction of his project, a tree house in a giant madrone tree, built well above the practical climbing ability of most adults. I wondered why he was outside when the rest of the kids were in, and was espe-cially curious as to why he had gone out the window instead of the door.

Later, I found out that his teacher, Heather (a Scottish country woman), had been practicing some old-world disciplinary tech-niques to try to elicit more concentration in reading and writing skills from her students. Nadja took on the challenge, put her nose to the paper, and raised her pencil like a true scribe. But Jeb took issue with such tactics, so while the teacher's back was turned, he opted for an easy escape route—a quick scramble to the windowsill and a drop to freedom.

Actually, it was only through the patient attention of his mother that Jeb ever learned to read at all, first by deciphering "Calvin and Hobbs" (he could read the word transmogrify before he could read the word train) and later by reading "The Hardy Boys." The deal was that Mayche would read a page out loud (at a normal reading pace and with feeling) and then it was Jeb's turn to read a page (lots of sighs, sounding out, expertly inventing whole passages, starts and stops). In this manner, Jeb eventually learned to read, and all of us were delighted to finally be able to solve "The Mystery of the Disappearing Floor."

One bright morning, Nadja was sitting near the front door of the yurt, in the midst of a patch of pansies and daisies. She had on a red bandana and her long platinum blonde hair flowed down her back. On her knee rested a drawing pad. She was illustrating a daisy that she'd found growing in the grass. Her heart was so gentle, she would never have thought of actually picking the flower, so in order to get an adequate view, she was hunkered right up close to it. As she worked, she spoke lovingly to the flower. "Oh," she said, "you are so cute! I will draw you just the way you are!" In her lap, with legs outstretched into the grass, lay a baby goat, completely relaxed, white, with little yellow eyes like slits in the sunshine.

During this time, I was working on a new garden, this one to be made up solely of medicinal herbs, which were my main passion. I tilled a large circle out in the field and amended the soil with aged goat manure from the barn. Scrimping, salvaging, and clap trapping, I had managed to acquire enough irrigation parts to run a gravity-fed line from Bird's Eye Pond (a deep-blue jewel of cold and very swimmable water located up toward Grayback Mountain) down to the garden site.

The irrigation was complete, with three sprinklers on tall risers set up equidistantly inside the new garden, securely wired to metal fence posts. I carefully shoveled up the soil from the pathway onto a continuous raised bed, making it in the shape of a giant spiral. It seemed appropriate that a diverse garden of medicinal herbs, with their strong personalities, would be tied together in a continuous bed, so that the energy could spiral in to the center (self-healing) or out to the cosmos (healing others).

The garden was made up of 42 species, with elecampane and giant yellow hyssop at the far-flung outer edge and the inevitable echinacea, calendula, valerian, and other common herbs spiraling in to the central nexus, where balloonflower was planted. The entire family awaited the first blooming of this (then) oddity with much anticipation. On the outer edge, in a low spot, I planted wild indigo, but it didn't like the moisture, so soon died. Happily, most of the species were thriving.

On this particular day, I had just finished weeding everything. Feeling munificent, I had started with the balloonflower and moved out to the giant yellow hyssop (which was making a strong show, unconcerned by the fact that nobody knew how to use it). Nadja was busy with her drawing pad and goat, but the rest of the kids had been amusing themselves by climbing trees near the outhouse, anticipating the moment when some unsuspecting parent would feel the call of nature, enter the structure, and sit down.

Waiting until what they deemed was precisely the right instant, the children would then pelt the corrugated steel roof of the outhouse with a barrage of twigs and green apples. The entire point, of course, was to cause the precipitous exit of the occupant and hopefully to catch a glimpse of their bewildered face. If the pants were down around the knees and a flapping banner of toilet paper trailed from one hand, well then, all the better! I couldn't help chuckling a bit at this crude spectacle, but the children, vastly amused, were producing uninhibited gales of laughter!

Eventually, everyone on the land was clued-in, the flow of traffic to the outhouse trickled to a stop, and the children got tired of waiting. Jeb, Sena, and several of their friends (including Stardust, Meadowlark, River, and Tarragon) climbed down from their perches and came pattering on their bare feet out to where I was working in the spiral garden. I was barefoot, too. The soft dirt of the pathways was no place for shoes.

Calling out the all-encompassing childhood invitation, "Come on!" Jeb initiated a new game—a riotous chase consisting of a line of running, pushing, and stumbling kids, starting at the outer edge of the spiral and winding in to the center. When the leader could go no further (I shuddered for the safety of the balloonflowers), he or she would then turn around, face the others, throw up his or her arms and scream. Then, everyone else would scream, reverse direction, and spiral full-tilt back out to the edge.

I moved off to the side and watched. It looked like so much fun that Nadja set aside her goat and drawing pad and joined in. Even Flow, the white sheep dog, got into the act,

bounding and barking from off toward the barn and entering into the frolic. Now plants were being knocked over, and a few feet and dog paws plunged alarmingly into the newly weeded beds. Seeing this, I almost called a stop to the party, but then held myself back. I suddenly realized that the children had discovered the essence of the garden—in to the center, out to the cosmos—celebrating happily as part of a healthy community of living beings.

Mayche stepped out the door of the yurt and called everyone in for supper—baked potatoes from our own garden and omelets with green onions, the eggs laid by our own chickens. There would be pansy petals smiling out from the edges of the plates. The children ran in, but I stayed behind to mound up dirt around a few bent stems and fill in the depressions of foot and paw.

I worked from the outside in. The garden felt warm and full of magic. Somehow, in the midst of all the joy, a rift had been repaired in me—I think it was "Mr. Yell-at-the Kids-for-Tromping-in-the-Garden" that had yielded to the greater good. All at once, I perceived the full breadth of the healing potential of the garden of medicinal herbs, and I knew that bringing gardens and herbs to the people would be my life's work.

Feeling suddenly very light of foot, I abandoned the path, jumping over first one raised bed and then another. I bent down to twist the valve that sent all three sprinklers singing in unison. Rainbows arched forth and dissolved. My newly weeded plants lifted their leaves turgidly in the mist. A chicken clucked. The aroma of baked potatoes and fried green onions wafted across from the yurt. I went in.

In 1989, we moved from Horizon School to our new land, where Munger's Creek never stops running and rarely gets too big for its bridges. In honor of our communal roots, we called the new land "Horizon Herbs."

Here we found plenty of habitats for growing medicinal herbs, including open land with sun and forest with shade. Together we made our gardens, built a home, then a greenhouse, then the seed house, and finally the rock walls. Jeb built a new tree house.

We didn't leave the spiral behind, either, because we redug it as our first garden on the new land. The plants expanded out from there, no longer just 42 species, but 10 times that many, and more. We collected lots and lots of seeds (sometimes plucking them one-at-a-time) and distributed them to other gardeners (and still do), as an extension of the idea of healing with the medicinal spiral.

The kids eventually matured, left home, and pursued their own lives in far-flung places. But, they haven't changed so much. Sena still loves to get dressed up (she's a world-class fashion model). Jeb still hammers (he builds very big things). Nadja still focuses in (she's a chemistry professor, doing medicinal plant research).

The original golden dragonfly has left behind generations of progeny, perhaps a little more red-gold than the first, but no less magical. It occurs to me that the golden dragonfly might not be so unusual, after all. Perhaps many of you gardeners out there have one. I hope you do. We're all doing the same work, you know, healing the earth with our gardens. And, as for turning the head upside down, I've never seen another dragonfly do this trick, but from time to time, it's a recommended procedure for us all.

PART 1

PRINCIPLES OF NATURAL GARDENING TECHNIQUES

CHAPTER 1 — OBSERVATION IN NATURE

Walking in nature and observing plants is a delightful activity that can take place either in the wilds or in the garden. The information gained on these observational walks is the first step in learning to cooperate with nature when growing medicinal herbs. Observation in nature is an especially significant technique for success in the cutting-edge work of domestication of wild medicinal plants. Natural factors, such as: native range; life cycle; seed dissemination; asexual reproduction; frost hardiness; sun, shade, and wind tolerance; water and drainage requirements; preferred soils; and plant and tree associations, are specific to each plant.

Understanding these factors can assist in developing a propagation strategy, improve plant placement, make clear what habitat modifications will be most useful for bringing wild plants into the garden, and reveal how to time these activities for maximum benefit.

Walking in the wild recharges the human batteries. This exercise must be good for the liver. I know it's good for the soul. The wildland hike gives you the opportunity to observe the way plants grow in their native habitat, which can certainly be a source of inspiration to us avid gardeners. Nobody gardens like mother earth. Watching carefully, you can learn directly from the plants, finding out whether they prefer to live alone or in groups, what kinds of companions they desire, what kind of soil they prefer, and what amount of sun and water they require. The growing conditions preferred by the parent plant are usually the conditions best suited for germinating its seeds. Carefully observing how and where plants self-sow and attuning to the cadence of plant growth cycles provides information that will serve to guide you in how, when, and where to plant the same herbs in the domestic garden.

Sowing the seeds of *Echinacea angustifolia.*
Years ago, when I first tried growing *Echinacea angustifolia*, I planted the seeds in the spring in a flat in the greenhouse, but nothing came up. Then, I made observations on how the plant self-seeds in nature. I discovered that these wild, mountain echinacea plants mature in late summer and the seed heads remain on the upright plant, in many cases all the way through to the first storms of winter. As the seed heads swell and contract with rain and sun, and when they are subsequently shaken by the wind, the seeds may easily come loose. Often assisted by the activity of small birds, viable seeds are scattered out onto the frozen ground or the snow.

The seeds remain cold and moist through the winter and are carried away from the plant by the spring melt. A few seeds are eventually deposited in disturbed soil or in the dirt-filled cracks between rocks. Then, as the ground warms up in the spring, these lucky few have the chance to germinate. So, the best method of starting the seeds in domestic culture is designed to mimic this natural process.

I tried again, this time sowing the seeds in an outdoor flat in the autumn, allowing the rain to fall on it, and the snows to snow on it, and in the spring was rewarded with little seedlings jumping up in the flat. Nature, I marveled, does things slowly and in her own rhythm.

The importance of sowing seeds in the fall.
As the years passed, I experimented with planting many other wild-derived medicinal herb species in outdoor conditions in the fall. Our first shadehouse was conceived largely out of the desire to have a forest-like haven for flats of germinating seedlings that needed to experience very cold and moist conditions, but also required protection. I found that in many cases, especially with herbaceous and woody perennials, the outdoor cold-conditioning method snatched the squiggling nugget of success away from the gnashing maw of failure.

Sowing seeds in the fall for germination in the spring is particularly applicable to slow or recalcitrant germinators native to the temperate north. This method captures the essence of germination as it occurs in the wild. Many times, this method gives success where other techniques give nothing at all! A few seeds that seem to respond best to this treatment are: aconite, black cohosh, Chinese coptis, devil's club, ginseng, goldenseal, yellow gentian, wild Job's tears, osha, *Rhodiola*, Virginia snakeroot, spikenard, and American wild yam.

Walking in the garden. A solitary stroll in the garden during the "off" season will reveal much about the regenerative habits of plants. There on the ground beneath where the love-in-the-mist grew, what are those little green sprouts—could it be the next flush coming up already? And there below the drying skeletons of the sweet corn, two different kinds of green rosettes appear, seemingly unfazed by the angular patterning of hoarfrost on manure-rich soil. On closer examination, they look like *Lobelia inflata* and another manure-lover known as shepherd's purse, both powerful medicinal herbs, both getting established before the dead-of-winter. If plants self-seed and germinate spontaneously in the fall garden, then isn't this a good indication of how best we can work with them when we seed them intentionally?

Another advantage of the garden walk is the way it sheds light on the status of plantings in process, providing necessary perspective on what works, what did not work, and what still needs to be done to *make* it work. In early December, I walk out on the land at Horizon Herbs. The land is a patchwork of bright green cover crops in various stages of expression, from the dark green peppering of germinating fava beans out in the far field, to a rich, water-filled, cold and crisp early planting of oats and peas in the middle field, already thigh-high and so turgid that they crackle.

The patchwork effect is an offshoot of a very good habit. The gardener spreads cover crop seed immediately after the plants are harvested from a particular bed or area. Since there are so many diverse rows and patches of herbs on the land, harvested at so many different times, well, the result is a very patchy, very lush, very green, ever-changing fabric.

Despite some frosty nights interspersed with a series of rain fronts that have recently doused the landscape, there are a few kinds of flowers going off, including a bright bed of johnny-jump-ups, wild calendula, and yellow calendula. Some of the larger carrot family plants, including asafetida and ashitaba, have newly awakened from the summer blahs and are sending thick stems and new leaves up out of the rain-softened earth.

I stop by to check the fall planting of zahir poppies (*Papaver somniferum*). The ground was tilled just prior to the first fall rains and the seeds were strewn in rows, leaving sufficient distance between them for the rototiller to pass for the purpose of weeding and cultivation. The poppies have now germinated, and are showing themselves as wide swaths of green on the earth. This was a planting that really worked out. It was planted a bit thick, though, and will need to be thinned before too long, to allow for the normal development of the plants. They will flower in the spring.

Is it time to turn the compost yet? I lift aside the tarp that is supposed to be keeping the compost dry and observe the pile. The washed cow manure seems quite dense and a bit too moist. I plunge in my hand. The surface of the pile is cold and clammy, but once my hand goes through the first layer of straw, there is some warmth. Plunging ever deeper, now up to my elbow, the compost begins to feel very warm indeed. This must be what it's like to give a cow a rectal exam. Then, my delving hand is abruptly halted by a layer of criss-crossed sunflower stalks that have not yet fully decomposed. "Well, that decides it," I say. "Can't turn the pile until those stalks break down, anyway." I grab a bit of the compost from well within the pile and bring it back out in my hand. It is full of squiggling earthworms. A tentative whiff reveals that the pile still smells a little poopy. All this means that the compost is not ready to be turned. I will check again later, but for now, I make a mental note to find a better tarp for that pile!

Placement of plants. When I first started growing eleuthero (*Eleutherococcus senticosus*), after patiently working the seedlings up in pots for a couple of years, I planted them in our "west garden" where they received a half-day of full sun. In the spring, they unfurled their leaves and my hopes soared like a barn swallow. But, I had not done my homework— eleuthero grows in Siberia, flourishing in thick stands around the margins of cold lakes. By midsummer in hot and dry Southern Oregon, those same tender leaves crisped on the plant like bread left too long in a toaster. That fall, I moved the suffering plants down into the shade of the trees by the creek. Planted in the cool forest loam, they came back fine. In subsequent years, the ants danced on the eleuthero flowers, and the branches grew heavy with fruit. I learned from this that the studied placement of plants is critical to realizing success in growing them outside their native range.

Experimentation. Designing specific studies to better understand things like habitat requirements of plants or germination of seeds can really help reveal the best places to put plants and the best ways to get seeds to germinate for you. Try filling two flats with different kinds of potting soil (one with lots of sand, one with lots of humus) and plant them with one kind of seed. This will help you learn what type of potting soil is best for that particular species.

Try planting seedlings of Chinese sage, for instance, in two different places. You might plant some in the shade behind the shed and some in the sun along the border of the driveway. Then, observe what happens to those plants—how they do or do not naturalize to their planting spots. This will help you determine the habitat requirements of the plant. Another good test might help elucidate whether fall planting or spring planting is preferred. For instance, you could sow wasabi seeds in the fall and then again in the early spring, and find out which method yields the best results.

Observation in the wild. Intent on visiting white sage in its native habitat, I pilgrimaged to eastern San Diego County in California. Parking the truck at the end of a sandy road, I hiked up between fragrant desert willow and desert lavender into the gray-green hills. The path wound between rounded boulders shouldering up out of sand that gleamed with quartz. Off in the distance, a roadrunner watched me warily from a rock. I avoided a pile of coyote poop where it disintegrated on a flat rock. The scat was loaded with juniper seeds, probably first consumed as juniper berries by a mouse, then the mouse consumed by the coyote; twice-digested, as it were. "Those would be easy to grow into juniper trees," I mused.

I was toting around two cameras, with a bottle of warm water protruding from my back pocket, under the proverbial burning hot sun, carefully keeping my distance from the barbed spines of the jumping cholla cactus. (Watch out!) Vultures wheeled overhead.

("Nope, I'm not dead yet!") Scrambling over those large, rounded boulders and following the dry creek beds up into the hills, away from all humanity, I soon spied up ahead the sweeping form of several mature white sage plants, rooted into the cracks between the rocks, flowering brazenly in the sun.

I savored this first encounter with white sage in the wild. Resting in the scanty shade of a desert fan palm, I watched as tiny hummingbirds visited the sages, their whirring wings the only movement in the entire landscape. I was trying to catch the hummingbirds at their nectarific play through the telephoto lens of my camera. The view finder kept fogging up with my sweat.

After snapping the photo, I tendered my apologies to the hummingbirds, interrupted their dance, and approached the white sage plants for closer examination. Their wonderfully spicy aroma surrounded them like an invisible shroud of peace. The recent parts of the raceme were flowering silvery-blue, while the older portions at the base were already dehiscing. Here, the dark brown seeds were visible and ready to shatter. Knowing that the adult plants had been dropping seeds, assumedly for years, I proceeded to examine every likely crack and cranny in the vicinity, but couldn't find any seedlings. In fact, I couldn't find any seedlings of—anything!

When making observations in the wild, I'm always looking for seedlings. Any signs of natural regeneration give a lot of information on how to domesticate the plant: when to plant the seed, how to make the proper potting soil, whether the plant prefers sun or shade for germination, how deep the seeds need to be planted, how much water to use when watering the seeds, and what fungal, plant, or tree associations may be significant factors in seed germination.

Walking further up the draw, I paid my respects to a spreading mormon tea (*Ephedra nevadensis*) and several comely bushes of yerba santa (*Eriodictyon* spp.) that had sprung up between the boulders. Then, I came upon an area where a flash-fire had erupted quite recently. This was evidenced by the charcoal on the desert floor, punctuated by the charred stumps of cacti and sage. Nearby, in the crevices of rocks, firmly rooted through the charcoal and ash, I found seedlings of white sage, their characteristically variegated arrowhead-shaped cotyledon leaves spreading to the sun . . .

Fire dependency. Back on the farm, with the help of my home-schooled girl, Sena, I proceeded to check my hypothesis about fire-dependency of white sage seeds. We prepared two deep, wooden flats, filling them with potting soil that contained a high concentration of coarse, sharp sand. We planted white sage seeds in little furrows in the flats, covered them sparingly with soil, and tamped it all down firmly. I'm a firm believer in tamping, you will come to know.

Then, we proceeded to build a little flash fire on top of one of the flats, using bits of kindling wood and pinecones. Sena stirred the fire with a stick, her eyes rooted to the crackling flames. The fire burnt out. Then, acting like a scant desert rain, we sparingly watered the flats. The other flat served as the requisite "control," so we treated it identically, but without the fire. Sena watched the experiment daily and was the first to see the seedlings emerging right through the whitened ashes of our flash fire.

Within three weeks or so, we had our results. Both flats contained healthy seedlings, but the seeds in the fire-treated flat had germinated faster and had produced seed-lings that were more vigorous and plentiful than the seedlings in the control. We had demonstrated that germination of white sage seed is *stimulated* by fire, but is not *dependent* on fire. Experiments like this really help convert information derived from observation in nature into useful methodologies for cultivating herb plants.

Certain plants have a reputation of being somewhat difficult to germinate and maintain in the garden. Among these, several very important medicinal herbs stand out: arnica, bloodroot, goldenseal, lomatium, osha, ashitaba, and yellow gentian to name a few. Rare plants are rare for a reason—they are in high demand, and they are hard to grow!

My work with cultivating rare plants has shown that the key to the treasure is available to those who will observe nature with careful attention. Planting in cadence with natural cycles produces seedlings that gain a secure sense of place. Such plants attain their maximum size, make plenty of seed, and produce potent medicine. In the end, it may be said that cooperating with nature produces self-sufficient plants, and that means less work for us humans!

CHAPTER 2 — WINDOWS OF OPPORTUNITY

Chuck's story. I am inspired by a story. It's about a homeless man named Chuck who made his bed under a freeway bridge in Portland, which is the big city in Oregon located many miles north of where we live. Having lost his family and his job, he took to wandering aimlessly through the city, accepting a free meal here, sitting on a bench by a fountain there, passing the time.

One spring day, he was crossing one of the major thoroughfares near the downtown area. Miscalculating the speed of the cars, he had to step lively to reach the median strip, which had been recently rebuilt and filled with new soil. He hopped over the curb, but when his boot sank unexpectedly into soft dirt, he stumbled and fell down on both hands, there between the opposing lines of traffic. Unharmed, he pushed himself back up, and as he rose, gathered up a fistful of soil in each hand. The dirt was soft and rich. Instinctively, he put the soil to his nose and smelled.

Suddenly the memory of his childhood on a farm in Ohio flooded back to him. It was spring, and his grandmother was preceding him on the path to the cornfield. She wore a simple farm dress and her thick, white hair was loosely braided and fell down her broad back, swinging slightly with her gait . . .

The man shook his head and the vision dissolved, but the experience left behind an unmistakable feeling that welled up in his heart—it was the urge to garden. His face broke into a pleasant smile. Passing motorists were sure he was insane. They shook their heads and clucked their tongues. Chuck took no notice. His smile was soon replaced by a thoughtful expression, the soil fell from his hands, and then and there he hatched a wonderful idea. He would plant that empty median strip with rows of corn!

Chuck eyed the swath of dirt between the yellow painted curbs. If he ran one row straight up the middle and made two more rows a scant six inches from the curbs, then he'd have three rows with two feet between each row—just about right. He wondered if such a thing would be allowed. Then, he straightened his back, a determined look came over his whiskered face, and he stated aloud to the traffic, "I'm going to plant corn here." And that's just what he proceeded to do.

He remembered where he'd seen a hoe in a trash pile and, having retrieved it, started to hoe his way down the median strip. Nobody hassled him. He was gardening. For the most part, nobody disturbs a gardener, I suppose because everybody appreciates gardens! Swinging the hoe time and time again, he fluffed up the soil between the curbs. The exhaust fumes that arose from the traffic didn't bother him too much—he was used to it. Despite the location, it felt good to work. He hummed, ignored the cars, and kept at it until dusk.

He made his bed as usual under the bridge. Cars zipped and pinged overhead, and trucks made the cement rumble. The loneliness, the cold, and the constant disruptions often conspired to bring on a recurring nightmare, a dream where he awoke on the train tracks, unable to move, a single light approaching . . . He would then awake again under the bridge, his face having slipped off the pillow onto the concrete. On this night, he was so excited that he could barely fall asleep. His plans for the next day coursed through his mind. His body, he noticed, felt good from the exercise. Eventually he yawned and stretched. Then, when sleep finally overcame him, he had a peaceful dream of his grandmother. She was squatting in the field, her brown hands push-

a car cruised him. He waved. They were seen to converse, then shrugged their blue-clad shoulders, waved back, and went on.

Now, this is my favorite part of the story, which says something not so much about the man, but about humankind in general. *Nobody disturbed him—or the corn.*

The corn grew. It rains a great deal in Portland, so irrigation was unnecessary. By midsummer, the corn had made a dense, green, knee-high patch. Now, cars slowed and drivers gawked at the strange spectacle. People felt a sense of connection to the project, and they no longer thought that the man was crazy. Chuck even made the evening news. The camera showed him with his hoe in hand, looking like a scarecrow in the midst of his corn. People volunteered to help, but it was a small garden. He shook his head at all inquiries, smiled a secret smile, and kept cultivating.

ing soil over the corn seeds that gleamed like citrine in the furrow. She was grunting a little, pushing down with the weight of her body, firming them in . . .

Having no money to buy seed, Chuck spent the better part of the next day picking up discarded bottles and cans, and then turned them in for the refund. This gave him sufficient change to buy some corn seed at the corner store. Ignoring the pangs of hunger in his stomach, he excitedly returned to his median strip, scored three deep furrows in the dirt, and planted his seeds. After a few days, warmed by the sun and the hot cement all around, the corn came up, making cheery little rows of light green spears, a mellow contrast to the alarming yellow of the curb.

Chuck smiled, wiped sweat from his forehead, and cultivated the little seedlings in just the way his grandmother had taught him so long ago. He removed weeds, fluffed the soil, and thinned out the young plants. The traffic zoomed by. Two police officers in

Chuck visited his corn plants every day and, as they grew, felt a sense of accomplishment. He danced like a marionette when the plants made tassels and dropped yellow pollen down onto the golden, tousled tufts of silk. Finally, the ears swelled with ripe kernels, and the day came to pick the first cob of corn. Feeling giddy, he pulled it free of the stalk, peeled away the husk to reveal even rows of plump kernels, and consumed it raw, right there in the midst of the patch. It was delicious! Then, he gestured triumphantly with the nubbly cob, holding it like a trophy above his head. People honked and cheered.

To me, the crux of this story is that if someone wants to garden, regardless of resources, location, or social status, there is always an opportunity to do so. All it takes is the proper motivation and some hard work. Those of us that have access to good land are very lucky indeed. I hope we can all be as resourceful as this homeless person in Portland who took the initiative to make a garden in the midst of traffic. Bless him and all those that garden!

Working within nature. During the winter months, this land tends to receive quite a bit of snow and rain, but we always expect to see a dryish period that occurs in February. Our spirits are lifted by the parting of the clouds and warm, bright days that are good for greenhousing. If the ground dries sufficiently, this weather affords us the opportunity to till and plant some cover crops or perhaps direct-seed some medicinal herb crops.

One year, the thaw arrived around the end of January and, by the first week of February, the soil was beginning to dry out. There was a patch of oats and peas out in the east field that was only about ankle high, so it was holding less water than many of the more developed cover crops, and consequently the ground was sufficiently dry to be tilled. Normally, when tilling in a cover crop, we like to give the land a rest between tillage and planting, to give the carbon and nitrogen time to reabsorb into the ground. In this case, there would be no time for that, because dark clouds were already billowing up over the mountains that separate us from the Pacific Ocean and the wind was gusting. Even if you couldn't feel the moisture in the air, the dark clouds and wind would be a reliable sign of precipitation, and we wanted to get our seeds planted ahead of the rain.

Sowing the seeds of astragalus. The rototiller surprised me when it sprang to life after the second pull. Maybe it was picking up some charge from the sky. I ran it down the driveway and turned toward the field. Soon, the tines bit into the lush cover crop. Before me, the nitrogen-rich cover was like a pretty green blanket. Behind me, the brown soil fluffed up like a soft mattress. I wanted to prepare a spot for a winter planting of astragalus. Astragalus was a good choice in this instance, because it germinates best in cold soils. The plant is a good candidate for direct-seeding, because it is tough and taprooted. This is one of the best wellness herbs in our *materia medica*, and it is in high demand.

The seed we were using came from the previous year's harvest. We scarified the seed by rubbing it on medium weight sandpaper. Astragalus likes calcareous soil, so we made a mix of rock phosphate, ground limestone, and oyster shell, and strewed this on the bed, then tilled again to work it in. That is how we do it. We feed the soil, and then the soil feeds the plants.

Having finished tilling, my gardening friend, Erich, and I glanced at the gathering clouds and without delay scribed a couple of generous furrows into the newly tilled ground. The wind began to gust as we dribbled the seeds into the furrows. Then we covered over the seed with a little soil and tamped the rows with the palms of our hands. The brown mattress was now peppered with potential. Finally, in order to mark the rows and provide even greater drainage, we made some trips to the sand pile and covered over the newly planted rows with a thin layer of coarse, sharp sand.

That night, lying in bed, I heard the first heavy drops patter against the roof. This eventually crescendoed to a potent drumming. When I envisioned those astragalus seeds out in the field, covered cozily by their carpet of sand, charging up with rain water, I really rejoiced. Later, when the seedlings pushed up through the sand and raised their leaves in the mists of early spring, the benefits of watching the cycles and catching the opportunities truly came home to me. The land was happy, the astragalus was happy, and so were we!

It's like that on a small farm. People think life must be rural and uneventful, but actually, there is excitement in this close relationship with raw nature. The ritual planting of squash seeds in the spring, the cultivation and care of plants through the summer, the heat of the sun, the respite felt when moist air moves in, the wheeling of the moon through the heavens as we work late into the evening to bring in the squashes before the first hard frost—this is a life that nurtures body and spirit.

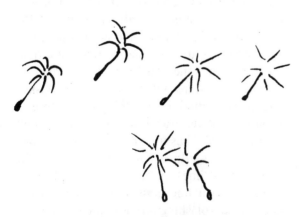

Windows of opportunity. One of the fastest growing things in a medicinal herb garden is the "to do" list. Lest the list begin to feel overbearing, I find it quite helpful to prioritize activities according to the doctrine of "windows of opportunity."

Over the years I've learned that activities like cutting back the perennials, growing the ashwagandha, harvesting the calendula flowers, or picking the heads from the sunflowers, is most efficiently accomplished while the window of opportunity for that activity is wide open.

For instance, I prune back woody perennials such as lavender, hyssop, and sage in the autumn, after they have completed their seeding cycle. Snipping them back too soon in the summer would weaken the plants or compromise the seed harvest, and snipping them back too late would rob them of the precious energy invested in their swelling, springtime buds. So in this case, the window of opportunity is a long one—it opens just after seed harvest and closes just before the plants awaken in spring.

A good example of a short window of opportunity would be calendula flower harvest. Each calendula flower lasts in its prime for only a few days. The window for harvesting that flower opens in the morning after the dew dries off and the flower fully opens, then closes in the afternoon along with the closing of the flower.

Hawthorn is one of the most giving trees to plant in the shelterbelt, or anywhere else in the garden, the yard, or on the farm where there is enough room. Hawthorns are often planted in parks, as they truly augment the landscape with their midsize, fountaining form. Planted closely in a row, hawthorns can be shaped into tall, tough hedges. The medicinal flowers of hawthorn attract myriads of pollinators to the garden and are useful, in their own right, for making a heart-tonic tincture or tea. These flowers are best picked at the early "ball" stage, when they are just forming and are not rain wet. If you pick them wet, they will discolor and lose their fragrance upon drying. If it's a rainy week around hawthorn flower harvest (and somehow this always seems to be the case), then the harvest window may slip open for only an hour or two, in the late afternoon when a gap in the storm clouds is opened up by a warm wind, and the flowers air dry. When this happens, get going, it's time to pick!

Ashwagandha is a desert or tropical perennial grown as an annual in the temperate north. Growers are acutely aware of the need to extend the growing season in order to obtain a large, mature root by fall. So, the window of opportunity for sowing the seed would be during the first good greenhousing weather of the New Year, when the bright winter days send the temperature inside the solar greenhouse soaring to the point where these heat-loving germinators will jump up in the flats.

When the seedlings attain their second set of leaves, then they may be pricked into pots. If this is accomplished in good time, then the seedlings increase nicely in size and will readily survive the rigors of planting to the field when the soil warms up in the spring. This results in big roots at digging time, which can be equated to big medicine.

In the case of sunflower seed harvest, I learn from the birds. Without their help, it's a little hard to know when the seed is really ready. Green sunflower seed may look plump and tasty, but, if picked during this stage, the kernel will shrivel and dry up, instead of curing.

Instinctively, the birds know when the seed is fully ripe, and they don't generally consume it until it's mature. So, I wait until the crows begin the harvest, pecking out the seeds, leaving cavities in the outer margins of the sunflower disk that appear like the hole left behind when a tooth falls out. Once I see this, then I know it's time for harvest—I use my machete to cut off the giant, disk-like heads, laying them in the sun to dry and after-ripen. Finally, I rub the heads on a coarse table screen to disengage a flurry of fat seeds.

Dandelions open their mature seed heads, one at a time or in clusters, all at once on a sunny afternoon. These puffballs may remain attached to the placenta for a day or two, but soon release their parachuted progeny, which fly off on an errant wind. The plant is all about the spring. It is one of the main herbs of spring, effective in clearing toxins from the liver. The seed of dandelion remains easily sproutable for only a few brief weeks, also in the spring. If stored for a month or two, the dried seed will take on dormancy, which makes it difficult to sprout. Therefore, the best approach is to harvest the seed when it is ready, and plant it as soon as possible after harvest.

Working within windows of opportunity is productive, in that tasks done on time are likely to be accomplished efficiently. For instance, it's much easier to remove immature weed seedlings from a raised bed with a stirrup hoe than to wait three weeks and pull tall weeds by hand. I've learned that, in general, after the window of opportunity is closed, it does little good to try to pry it open again. For instance, there's little advantage in cutting back perennials after the new spring growth has begun to form, since the plant is then robbed of some of its power. There's little advantage in sowing, pricking out, or transplanting ashwagandha too late in the spring, as the roots will not attain sufficient size at harvest. Picking calendula blossoms too late in the season makes for poor quality and low yields of calendula flowers. And, once dandelion seed is released on the winds of chance, it has certainly flown beyond our grasp. With luck, it will volunteer nearby.

Working within windows of opportunity supports sanity. We do one thing at a time, ideally keeping the mind on the task at hand in a kind of working meditation. Every task is another opportunity to do things right, to contribute, to serve. Taken in this light, the long list of "to-do's" has little power to compromise our happiness. In my imagination, the completed tasks line up like a family of ducks waddling in a line across the green lawn of abundance, splashing one after another into the placid blue pond of "done."

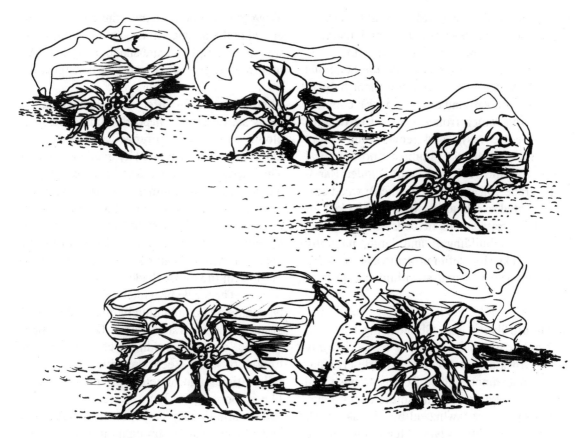

CHAPTER 3 — CREATING PLANT HABITAT

The universe loves edges—it's where stuff happens. If biological entities are going to interact, chances are it will happen along some kind of a margin, usually in an area of diverse resources where there is an abundance of sunlight and water. This might be the edge of the forest or perhaps a beach, stream, river, canyon, or ravine. This zone where one habitat melts into another is known as the "ecotone," a place of biological diversity. Such areas support a higher number of plant, animal, and insect species and tend toward environmental balance, due to the regulating influence of sun, soil, water, plants, and animals.

On a smaller scale, in the garden, we invite in as much habitat diversity as possible for the same reason—environmental balance leading to healthy plants, animals, and people. In the garden, we increase the surface area of useable space and define the planting areas by employing shelterbelts, hedgerows, raised beds, fences, trellises, trees, rocks, and the winding garden path. The protected beds around buildings are a particularly choice spot for favorite plants and plants that require ongoing attention.

We use inexpensive, organic, local, and whenever possible garden-derived materials for nourishing the plants and making specific microsites for them. The shadehouse, greenhouse, outdoor propagation beds, outdoor raised beds, and the garden itself constitute the most important areas for germinating and growing the plants. It is up to the gardener to create this whole environment, using sweat and good intentions. The garden is created for the plants, openly accessible to humans. We take great measures to support the growth of preferred species. In so doing, the gardener creates plant habitat.

Basic materials for building plant habitat. Much will be said about methods and materials later on this book. At this point, I think it's worthwhile to mention a few of the materials that are most useful in creating plant habitat. They are: coir (ground coconut husk); compost (of course); mulch (rotted sawdust or decomposed tree leaves); sand (coarse and sharp, from local quarries); pumice (horticultural grade volcanic rock, 3/8 inch); cinder (landscape grade volcanic rock, 3/8 inch); weed barrier (layered cardboard); concrete blocks (for building infrastructure of beds, walls, greenhouses, and buildings); and large, naturally shaped rocks (for defining pathways, building beds, lining walls, and absorbing the heat of the sun).

A tale of Silver City. Shimmering waves of heat pulsed from the highway as I drove my pickup truck across Arizona. The desert landscape, miles upon miles of creosote bush, red sandstone, saguaro, and mesquite under a surreal, turquoise sky, whizzed by. I was on my way to Silver City in New Mexico, where I'd been invited to give a talk. Arriving at night, I made my camp by the side of the road and fell asleep in the desert starlight. The next day I proceeded into Silver City and found my venue, a little herb shop on Bullard Street. People filed in and seated themselves on folding chairs while I nervously fiddled with a few herb samples up front. There was a television camera going. Someone asked me to give my best piece of advice on how to garden in the harsh desert conditions of the Southwest.

I answered by first asking a question "Where do you find the greatest biological diversity here in the desert?" "In the deep canyons," someone answered. "So what is it that makes the deep canyons so special?" I asked. "Cool shade at midday!" came the reply. Then someone else piped up with "Water!" A dreadlocked fellow in the back row stood and said "If you go down into the canyons, you can find lots of growing things, thistles, bumblebees, jackrabbits—they all get

along pretty good in the canyons." So the crowd really answered its own question, which was quite simple: create shade and you'll promote water; give water and you'll support life.

Shade, water, and life. The shadehouse can be as simple as a few poles holding up shade cloth, with plants arranged underneath on tables or in beds, irrigated by overhead misters. The shadehouse is a prime example of plant habitat created by humans. In the Southwest, where water and shade are at a premium, such a structure becomes an indispensable tool for gardening. Plants that would shrivel up and die in the dry heat of the outdoors thrive turgidly in the moist shade.

The shade provided by shade cloth can be augmented by planting bioregionally appropriate shade trees and vines. Good examples for the desert would be chaste tree and tronodora. To keep the soil alive during fallow times and to retain the precious water like a sponge, low-lying, water-retentive, and soil-building cover crops, such as buckwheat and clover, can be brought into the system. This is one way to turn the desert into an oasis.

When cultivating a vegetable garden, the conditions required for success are pretty well understood—sun, water, fertile soil, and good seeds. Start your vegetables in the spring and harvest them in the fall. When cultivating a rare and unusual medicinal plant, however, the conditions required for success may not be so simple. The rare plant enthusiast tunes into specific germination techniques, custom soil mixes, particular combinations of shade and sun, watering according to a special schedule, and often cultivates the plant for years before seeing the first flower.

Microniches. Any given piece of land may look homogenous to the casual observer, but upon closer examination you can discover various microniches. Soils may or may not be consistent. Depending on how the soil was made and how it has been taken care of, there may be areas with loam, sand, clay, or rock.

Each one of these areas will support different kinds of plant life, so it is important to recognize the variations, and make use of them. For instance, an area in the part shade with deep, rich soil is perfect for jiao-gu-lan. Soil that contains undigested woody debris is excellent habitat for osha. An area of calcareous soil at the outer margin of the sprinkler, which would normally not receive enough water even to grow a squash, is perfect for growing *Lomatium*. And so it goes. You become aware of the microniches, and you find plants that will thrive best under those specific conditions.

Tricks to improve overwintering. Some folks in the temperate north have difficulty overwintering plants that grow wild in the Mediterranean basin, such as rosemary and the various varieties of lavender. The climate preferred by such plants is hot and dry in the summer and cool and rainy in the winter. However, many of us live in places that are hot and humid in the summer and frozen up in the winter. In such cold winter areas, Mediterranean plants can often be successfully overwintered by planting them in fast-draining soil on a southern exposure. It is particularly helpful to situate them against the south wall of a house, building, or stone wall. To increase drainage and heat retentiveness, the plants can be carefully weeded, and then a thick sand mulch applied under them, right up to the stem. This practice discourages regrowth of weeds and helps to keep the sensitive crown dry. The sand reflects light up into the plant. All these factors can spell survival for a plant that would otherwise succumb to the cold, moist conditions of winter.

There are all kinds of people interested in growing the rare and unusual, ranging from the home hobbyist growing the South African plant, hoodia, indoors to the medicinal herb farmer trying to grow a field of the alpine plant, yellow gentian, at elevation in the Rockies. Nevertheless, there is one thing the two hold in common—they must discover exactly what their plants require to be healthy and productive. If success is their goal, then they mustn't mind the effort it takes to make it all happen. Perhaps the following story about my experiences with mandrake (*Mandragora officinalis*) will further illustrate this point.

Mandrake story. Oh, how I yearned to successfully grow mandrake. Rarity of rarities, if she would but grace my garden, surely then I would be happy. I wanted to have this plant because it was difficult to grow, as well as being rare and unusual. I wanted it because of its strange looks, its biblical history, its long use in magic and medicine, and because, in truth, I knew so little about it. I wanted it because of the sound of its name.

Mandrake! I longed to become familiar with its flowers, fruits, and (gulp) seeds. The seeds, so plump and brown, disappearing into sandy, alkaline potting soil that I had mixed by hand, hoping to approximate the soils of its native habitat. How lovingly I planted those seeds, three by three, an inch deep in gallon pots, carefully tamping the soil. I set the pots, five in a row, in the best possible location, at the east end of the shadehouse—sunny, a bit dry, but protected. I watched, watered the pots when they got dry, and waited, and . . . waited.

After a year, in the early spring, the first sprouts appeared. The seedlings were no disappointment. They were as big as a hawthorn sprout, with long, pointed cotyledon leaves on a thick stem. Like ballet dancers, they extended their narrow leaves to the filtered sun and they grew—but oh so slowly—that first year. Then, early in the summer, they died back down to the root, but I never gave up faith. I knew the roots were down there, waiting. "Never," I told myself, "Never intercede with the cycles of plants. They have the wisdom. Now you, you have the patience. Be patient. No digging. They will rise up once again."

I didn't see them again until the New Year, in February, when they showed themselves once again, larger and stronger now, growing at a time of year when almost all the other plants on the farm were deeply dormant. I weeded the pots and stirred the soil around the softly pointed leaves that emanated from the swollen crowns. Within a few weeks, each plant produced several healthy leaves. They looked pretty good all the way through to May, but in June, they dropped their leaves again for the (now familiar) summer dormancy.

By the third year, the soil in the pots had shrunken way down, so when the plants went dormant I depotted them, stretching out the potbound roots and replanting them in fresh soil, each to its own gallon pot. The roots were about the size of my thumb. I was quite familiar with the folklore about how mandrakes will moan and scream and whatnot at harvest and, I admit it, I hesitated superstitiously when first depotting them. However, there were no screams upon transplant.

The next winter the mandrakes emerged again, and I asked myself if they were now robust enough to survive the rigors of being planted outside. The answer was only "Maybe." I needed more information on just what kind of outdoor conditions would make them thrive.

I visited a local friend, Daniel, who knew mandrake intimately, as he'd lived among them in their native habitat in the Middle East. I asked Daniel the obvious question "Where does it like to grow?" And the answer came," Out in the open, among rocks, in alkaline soil." "How much rain does it get?" I asked. "Not much," came the answer. Daniel unconsciously patted the skull cap that perched on top of his head, turned his long face toward me and fixed me with his large, watery, slightly bulbous eyes. "This isn't going to be easy," he said. I replied, "I know. Thanks for the info. I'm gonna make it happen!"

Back home I went, determined to make good use of Daniel's experience with the native habitat. I found a place in the full sun, slightly elevated and thus well-drained from the winter rains and out of the reach of my summer sprinklers. In this place, I laid down a weed barrier of cardboard and then covered the area with coarse sand—wheelbarrowful after wheelbarrowful.

I took five big rocks and plunked them down in the sand, arranged in a deliberate curving line, with the most perpendicular face of each rock oriented north, so as to throw a good shadow. Then, in the shadow next to each rock, I dug a hole through the weed barrier. Into this hole, I put a little compost, two handfuls of sand, and then a huge double handful of ground limestone. While I did this, sand fell in from all around and I dug it all in as best I could with a spade. Finally, I got down on my hands and knees and worked it by hand, until the hole was filled with very well blended limey and sandy soil. Into this improbable mixture, I transplanted the mandrakes from their gallon pots, muttering my usual "Grow baby grow," swirling the pure sand back in around the crowns, leaving the dog-tongue-like leaves lapping up the shade of the rocks.

The leaves held on for a few days, but with the first hot days of summer, they dried up, eventually blowing away in a vagrant wind. Through the long summer I waited and into the fall, resisting the recurring urge to dig down and check the crowns. In winter, snow made soft hummocks of the rocks.

One bright day in late January, it was as if I was called to the spot, and on close examination, I found each plant pushing through the sand mulch, five blunt spearheads of dark green, tightly rolled leaves. By February, upright clusters of silvery-lavender flowers pushed up between the leaves. Each flower sported a bed of yellow stamens and one or two curving pistils.

At first, I thought there were no native pollinators that worked this plant, and also postulated that the early flowering was occurring prior to the appearance of most pollinators. Then I discovered, on very close examination, that the flowers were a play-bed of tiny, jointed, crawling insects, nearly invisible to the naked eye, coursing like miniature ships over the surface of the flowering parts of the plant. When I discovered this, it made *my* skin crawl, also, and I wondered if these creatures could be the pollinators.

Not taking any chances, I used a soft brush to hand-pollinate the flowers, first titillating the stamens, and then swirling the brush around the receptacle. I was curious if there was any pollen actually being applied, so I took the brush into my office and examined it under the microscope. There was no pollen on the brush—not a good sign.

I watched for about two weeks and kept visiting the plants whenever the sun was bright and I knew the flowers would be open. During the course of this time, many of the original blossoms died away, although others appeared to have been pollinated, because the shriveled flowers were giving way to swollen, marble-sized green fruits. Other flowers were still forming and opening and, as I tried to pollinate them, from time to time, I would see a very small amount of yellow pollen going onto the brush—a good sign.

Then after about three weeks, on a bright day, I noticed a few half-opened flowers on some of the larger plants and went at it again with my paintbrush. Suddenly, a whole plume of pollen cut loose, and the brush was covered with yellow about a third of the way up (it was a small brush, the kind one finds in a kid's paint set). I worked the pollen around among all the flowers. They waved their curved pistils, the spongy yellow-green terminations like open palms dusted in yellow.

Then, I took the brush back to my microscope. On the vastly magnified hairs of the brush, I could see little globes of pollen that adhered singly and in globs. They appeared to be silvery colored, much like the color of the flowers themselves. It surprised me that by far the most pollen was being produced very late in the flowering cycle. Why would this be?

Within a few weeks, frosts having no adverse effects, the dark, shiny green, delicately savoyed, prominently veined leaves unfolded into large, handsome rosettes (similar to chard, but nearly stemless and decidedly less tasty). The leaves shouldered up over the rocks, spread out across the sand, and looked right at home. Slowly, as spring gave way to summer, the fruits grew, swelled ever larger, softened, and eventually matured. I was ecstatic. I discovered through trial and error that it was best to allow the fruits to remain under the protective umbrella of the leaves; otherwise they were apt to pick up a (nonfatal) sunburn. I was biding my time, in order to assure that the precious seeds inside the fruits would be fully developed at harvest.

During the first week of July, some nocturnal critter purloined one, then another of the fruits. (For weeks, I was on the lookout for scat containing mandrake seed, which, of course, I would have pounced on, like a crow after a grasshopper.) To prevent further loss, I picked the remaining fruits. They detached readily from the thick stem, which remained on the plant. A careful examination of the stem showed a pentamenous (5-pointed) calyx with a seal in the center, a perfect representation of the sun, complete with radiating rays of light.

The ripe fruit was about three inches across, nearly round, turgid, with a thick, green skin. I tasted one, and found the fruit to be very tasty, sweet, and a bit acid, with no inebriatory effects, even after consuming a fair amount.

(However, later, I did notice a marked laxative effect!) The smell and taste varied according to the ripeness of the fruit.

Among related plants, the closest fruit, in terms of size and appearance, would be the tomatillo. The skin of the mandrake is thicker, the internal pith is much less watery, and the seeds are much larger in the mandrake than the tomatillo. The smell is reminiscent of honeydew melon, taking on an exotic, intoxicating perfume as the fruit ripens. This perfume is not unlike the deep aroma of a woman's gravid belly, and perhaps from this primeval odor arose the tradition of using mandrake to promote fertility.

I have given this account of mandrake cultivation mainly because it illustrates just how persistent a hobbyist can be when creating the habitat for a prized plant. And, it is not only the habitat that must be right—it also requires a feel for the right *timing* in order to successfully introduce the plant to its niche. I realize that there is a modicum of madness in this pursuit, and would like to reassure the reader that there are easier plants to grow and there are easier ways of creating habitat for them. Of course, it is more work to develop habitat for an exotic plant than to create habitat for a plant that already thrives in the bioregion.

The second part of this book will give very specific advice on ways to increase plants and methods and materials for creating plant habitat. Just for now, please suffice it to say that if you build healthy soil for plants and you put good organic seeds there, you can expect miracles to happen.

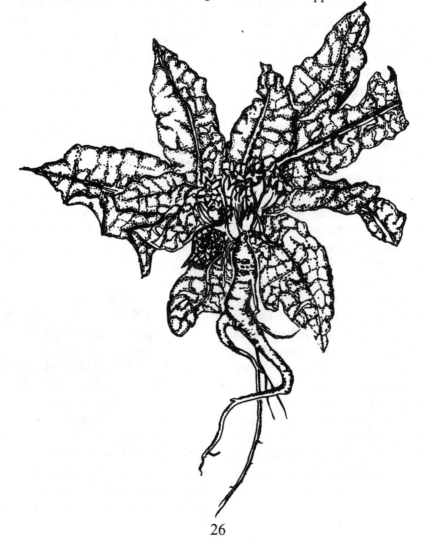

CHAPTER 4 — BENEFITS OF DIVERSITY

Diversity breeds balance. Mourning doves, with their peaceful yet melancholy litany, often remind me of the interconnectedness of living beings in the garden. Maybe it's because their cries lead me to contemplate death, and in so doing, I naturally develop an appreciation for life.

Milk thistle story. One February I was watching closely the weather patterns, and after a few bright days determined that the ground had dried sufficiently to allow tillage without unduly harming the structure of the soil. Taking advantage of this window of opportunity, I was out there with my rototiller, making the skeletal summer weeds disappear, preparing a seedbed for rows of crops that I would plant in the spring. Besides the dead annual weeds pigweed and crabgrass, there were also leftovers from my annual seed crops, the dried stalks of love-in-the-mist and safflower. I also tilled in many a healthy milk thistle rosette, almost as meaty as cabbages, some as large as three feet across, plants that had volunteered at random in the field.

The more milk thistles I tilled in, and the more I thought about what a healing seed the milk thistle makes, the less enthusiastic I was to get rid of them. I hadn't cultivated a good patch of milk thistle for a couple of years—surely it was time to renew my supply of seed. No, I couldn't till in every one of those beautiful, fleshy but spiny rosettes, so hopeful they were, waiting for the warming of spring to bulk up like bodybuilders. Bigger than people, they were full of unembraceable life, nourishing their treasure trove of elongated, shiny black, hepatotonic seeds. milk thistle finally won out over my (perhaps) more prudent destructive impulses, and I preserved a double 50-foot row out there in the middle of the field, with generous spacing on either side and between the plants. I knew full well that harvesting the seed by hand would be a difficult job, but was also thinking of the great good the seeds would do, as medicine for the people.

The spring progressed into early summer. I weeded and watered my milk thistle patch, and the plants responded accordingly,

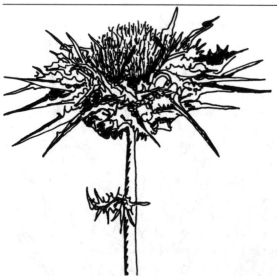

filling the spaces and raising their spines in polyheaded glory. The purple crowns of the flowers kissed the sun as the weather warmed into late spring. Then, the flowers faded and dried, replaced by the first white tufts of pappus hair—gossamer parasols tugging on fat, black seeds.

On a sunny afternoon, I approached that gargantuan patch with buckets and shears in hand and gingerly snipped my initial harvest of spiny capitula—three heaping bucketfuls. With one thing and another taking precedence, in the ensuing days I neglected to continue to harvest the bounty. Driving by a few weeks later, I guiltily surveyed the patch, and noticed with a shock that it was now releasing copious quantities of viable seed into the rest of my gardens and over the fence onto Mr. Barleywater's overgrown front pasture.

In my mind I went over the possible scenario. There he'd be, Mr. Barleywater, as unmistakable as a yeti, out in his front pasture for a rare appearance, his khaki pants hiked up high on the waist, held in place by a deteriorated black leather belt with a tarnished buckle. He'd lift his reading glasses up off the crown of his nose with one hand and peer nearsightedly below them, across toward the tangle of green that is my farm, his impossibly unkempt and wiry eyebrows magnified menacingly by the glasses, furrowed in concentration. Then he'd clear his throat.

"Ahem," he'd say to catch my attention, and I'd skulk over to the fence, like a schoolboy approaching the lectern for a scolding. Then he'd query, "Can you identify these plants that have sprung up in my pasture?" I'd say, "Um, let me see now," with finger held quizzically to the side of my jaw. "Why, those look like milk thistles! I wonder where they could have come from? Then, hoping to divert his attention, I'd gaze up at the fir trees where the mourning doves huddled in sympathetic silence. Then, I'd begin to whistle distractedly, "Doo de doo . . ."

I started up out of my daydream, and gave the neglected patch a careful appraisal. The ground underneath the milk thistles had turned downy white with the fallen pappus, piled about four inches thick, evenly distributed around the spiny trunks of the plants, resting in gentle mounds like a freak snowfall. I thought of how many seeds lay trapped in that gossamer carpet, and then envisioned all the seedlings they would make. I saw myself weeding them out of the carrots. I had no alternative plan, except to harvest the remaining seed as best I could.

Then nature came to my rescue. Every time I walked past the patch, maybe with bucket in hand bound for harvesting the calendula seed, or making noise, pushing my weed trimmer to open up the trail along the back fence, in short whenever I disturbed the area, I would flush out the resident family of mourning doves. There were six of them. As plump as partridges, they would immediately lumber off through the air, barely able to launch their fat bodies, producing the little chuckling noise they make when they fly. Their resting cry is a funeral dirge, that's for sure, but in flight they sound like plump schoolchildren twittering nervously in the choir over an unclaimed fart, "He-he-he-he (not me, not me) he-he-he-he." The birds would set their course for their favorite perch, up inside the protective fir trees that tower above the wrecked cars abandoned in front of Barleywater's place. Soon, their melancholy cries could once again be heard.

Later, I would find them back down in the milk thistle. They were gorging on the seeds. Every seed they ate, I realized, was one less volunteer seedling for me to pull, one less reason to worry about what Mr. Barleywater might say. So you see, the balance was being maintained despite my shortcomings. In a diverse garden, this usually is the case. Human input is far from the whole story.

In the end, I collected plenty enough new seed to fulfill my requirements for the year. Mourning doves never sound happy, but in actuality they were full of seeds, and they were *very* happy. The plants were happy. I was happy. It was all a good trade.

Diversity breeds resiliency. Chauncey, in Iowa, planted a half acre each of *Echinacea angustifolia*, goldenseal, and marshmallow. He worked away at his plantings, and things were coming along pretty well. Then around midsummer, it started to rain and, as is often the case in the Midwest, whoever was responsible for turning off the faucet was out to lunch, dinner, and breakfast too. By the time it stopped raining, the Mississippi had jumped its banks and low-lying fields of corn and soybeans looked like lakes.

Chauncey's *Echinacea angustifolia* started, sputtered, and then died of crown rot. The goldenseal, protected by the forest and being a plant that really loves water (they don't call it "*Hydrastis*" for nothing), did just fine. And the marshmallow, the marshmallow *loved* the extra water. By fall, Chauncey had to bring in a big tractor to lift the marshmallow roots, which looked a little like those giant squids that accidentally get caught up in the nets of Japanese deep-sea trawlers. This story demonstrates that in planting medicinal herbs, it makes economic sense to hedge your bets and plant a few different crops. You never know what the weather will do, what will thrive, and what will not. However, the reasons for planting diversity go beyond simple economics.

In nature, plants grow as part of an interdependent ecosystem, usually composed of (among other biological entities) trees, bushes, grasses, and interspersed patches of broadleaf plants. When the medicinal herb garden contains all the elements of this natural ecosystem (as opposed to the monocrop), then mammalian and insect pests, although they exist, don't usually cause much damage. The naturally diverse array of plants makes up a garden for all beings, including pests and their predators and, as such, is innately self-regulating. Following find a couple of experiences that demonstrate the value of planting diversity to increase resiliency of crops when they are subjected to stressors.

The story of the raining tree. From early childhood, I was fascinated by stories of "raining trees." Long ago on the island of Heirro lived one such tree. This stony island, the westernmost of the Canary Islands, is pockmarked with hollows caused by ancient volcanic activity, and good drinking water is hard to come by. During the seventeenth century, above one such hollow on a hill, lived a raining laurel tree. By night this tree gathered water from the clouds, condensed it on its leaves, and rained it down under its branches. The water collected in the hollow, forming a clear pool of pure water. Eventually, this legendary source of drinking water became well-known to passing ships. An engraving of the raining tree even graced the cover of a contemporary herbal. Knowing this story, I have always looked out for raining trees on my travels. More than once, hunkered down in a sparse patch of shade in the midst of a desert in Africa or South America, I have bidden my tree to give off a cool mist—but to no avail.

The raining sunflower. Then, recently, in my own garden, I discovered a different aspect of this phenomenon. Several sunflowers had volunteered in a sandy stretch of land where I was growing white sage and guajillo peppers. As is often the case, these volunteer sunflowers,

raining plant! Then, with mounting curiosity, I grasped the tip of a leaf and lifted it up to reveal—a dense population of green aphids! There was a whole little aphid commune under there, everybody happily sucking plant juices and collectively emitting a fine green mist (from their little rear ends, as close as I could tell). Resisting the temptation to disturb the aphids in any way, I let the leaf drop back to its former position.

The bug balance. A few days later, I brought a friend to the (again dry) field, feeding his expectations with grandiose stories about raining trees and raining sunflowers, but as is so often the case, my expectations gave way to disappointment. The sunflower was not raining that day, and when I turned up the leaf of the plant, the reason became apparent. I found not only aphids, but also large red and black ants. The ants were milking the aphids, and the aphids no longer had any moisture to spare.

Over the next few days, under the stern mastership of the ants, the aphids dwindled. I noticed an increasing number of empty shells of aphids that had succumbed under the stress. Finally, the aphids, for the most part, disappeared and, without their servile cows, the ants soon followed suit. The sunflower, no longer hosting a mini-civilization, shrugged its leafy shoulders and lifted its developing head to the sun—healthy and happy.

I visualize the bell curve that describes this interaction. The population of aphids increases rapidly as the sunflower grows, culminating in the highest numbers just prior to the appearance of the ants. Then, as the ants take their toll, the aphid population diminishes until it again reaches baseline. The happy ending is that my raining sunflower eventually produced a heavy crop of seeds. By cultivating diverse plants in an organic system, we create habitat for both pest and predator. In many cases the appearance of a pest, followed by its natural increase and eventual dissolution, requires no overt reaction from the farmer.

emerging early from seed that had overwintered in the dirt, were much larger and healthier looking than the sunflowers I'd planted on purpose in a different place. It was high noon, and I was down on my knees, checking the ground to see if it needed watering. The top two or so inches of dirt was quite dry, and I had just decided to set up a watering cycle for that evening, when I noticed that, over to the side, the ground beneath one of the largest sunflowers was unaccountably moist.

Approaching this large-leaved, thick-stemmed plant, I minutely examined the ground. In exact coordination with the shape and lateral extent of the leaves, the ground beneath the plant was moist through-and-through. Extending my hand below the leaves, I was instantly cooled by a light green mist that emanated from the plant. A slow smile blossomed on my face. I could hardly believe I'd found it! If not a raining tree, then at least a

Deer. For many years we grew our medicinal herb gardens without a fence, and deer walked through the gardens daily, often bedding down in the orchard and drinking from our pond. We found that deer are browsers, not lawnmowers. They take a bite here and a bite there, eating and moving on. Deer like to eat soft, bland, and mucilaginous plants, such as plantain and purslane. They will eat apple leaves and blackberry leaves, which doesn't bother me a bit. They love windfall apples. They do not eat Mediterranean herbs such as thyme and rosemary, nor do they prefer a large array of other bitter, strange-smelling, or otherwise prickly or poisonous medicinal plants. Actually, planting densely and intermixing beds of preferred forage plants with beds of plants that deer will not eat is a way to protect the whole garden from fatal herbivory. (OK, OK, even back then, we kept our broccoli inside a fence.)

Eventually, we deer-fenced the whole farm, but in the autumn, I still let the deer come in. This is partly due to my wish to create a haven for the deer during hunting season and partly because autumn is a good time for the cleanup crew to make an appearance.

I was weeding the ma-huang. Nothing unusual about that—I have to do it about ten times a year. This time I was removing stumps of grass that had been knocked back by the frosts, pulling them from between the robust round spires of the ma-huang, where it emerged greenly from its bed of red cinders. I noticed that the sheep sorrel, which is usually really hard to remove from around the woody stems of the ma-huang, had been nipped back. I could see where the deer had nosed right in and snipped off the sheep sorrel seed heads and upper leaves.

Then, I moved over to the circle garden and noted that the gleefully spreading clovers had been nipped back, right where they were beginning to cover the aloe-like asphodel and the pretty *Iris* species known as orris root. Granted, a few of the orris root leaves had also been nipped, but this looked like collateral damage, what with the scrumptious clovers so close at hoof. There among the grasses, glistening blackly in the chilly afternoon light, was a pile of deer droppings, softly gleaming. "Looks like they've been eating apples," I mused. The droppings soon melted back in among the plants, a shot of nitrogen for spring.

31

The pepper monocrop story. My friend, Shelley, really wanted to make her living growing medicinal plants. She had a knack for gardening, and a love for hot cayenne peppers. In fact, her peppers (and her custom formulated blow-steam-out-your-ears cyclone cider) became famous around the region of Gila in New Mexico. Wanting to capitalize on this popularity, she planned her biggest pepper garden ever. The garden was watered by an irrigation ditch served by the Gila River, on a piece of rented ground surrounded by stock fence and located out in the open.

Shelley started her cayenne early in the spring in a tube greenhouse, meanwhile tilling and fertilizing her acre of ground, making it ready for the peppers. She transplanted when the ground had truly warmed up, and the plants grew quickly. Peppers have shallow root systems and appreciate frequent, light watering.

Shelley watered with rich river water and spent morning after morning barefoot in the field, with a wide-brimmed hat on, sturdy and determined, hoe in hand, removing the pigweed. She watched with mounting enthusiasm as the peppers dug in, bulked up, and began to pump out fat and waxy, white flowers.

Meanwhile, however, all around the pepper field, the surrounding land dried up, grasses turning from the green of the winter desert to a dusty brown. Shelley's garden started to look like a green postage stamp adhered to a big brown parcel. Grasshoppers living in the surrounding fields ran out of food and were magnetized to her peppers. At first there were a few hoppers, and then there were many, and with mounting alarm she realized that they were getting hungrier every day. Although she bravely fought them, letting them have it with a strong spray from her garden hose, Shelley's succulent cayenne eventually succumbed to those grating jaws.

Shelley stood at the edge of the field. Her hoe drooped. A grasshopper landed momentarily on her knee and looked up as if to say, "Got any more?" She brushed it away. The pepper crop was lost. She looked around her. A few more trees would have been nice, she thought. Tree leaves would have made alternative food for the grasshoppers, and trees would have been perching places for the crows, which eat grasshoppers. Perhaps a border of marigolds would have been a good idea, and it might have helped to alternate beds of peppers with beds of garlic (both ingredients of cyclone cider, by the way).

Shelley was visualizing her new garden, consisting of beds of several different crop plants surrounded by a shelterbelt of mixed woody species. She was thinking in the right direction, and applying these principles, in subsequent years, she pulled off some great crops on the same land. The garden of diversity is resilient in the face of stress, gives back what you put into it, and is a garden for all beings.

CHAPTER 5 — RULES OF GREEN THUMB

Too many people label themselves as unable to grow plants. This "brown thumb complex" can be overcome. It is our birthright to have positive relations with the plant world, and as breathers of air and consumers of salads, it is hard to deny our dependency on plants. To nurture plants is a great joy to be missed by none. Following find the ruling factors that turn brown thumbs to green and make green thumbs greener.

A few well-grown plants produce more than many poorly grown plants. It's all about nutrition. If a few plants are given sufficient space to grow and are properly cultivated, composted, and watered, regardless of how many of them there are, then they will give a higher yield than many plants that are starved for attention. For home medicinal use, with a few exceptions, 10 or 12 feet of bed space for a given species will give sufficient yield. Even if your garden space is small, I suggest growing a minimum of three of a kind. This gives a little insurance against losing a plant to the usual mishaps and besides, plants need friends.

It's not much work to plant some seeds. However, planting the seeds is just the beginning of your relationship with the plants, and, as the summer progresses, if you are trying to take care of *too many plants*, it may be hard to find the time to take care of them all. If you start small, you will probably find that the weeding, watering, harvesting, and medicine-making aspects keep you plenty busy until, well, about Christmas or so. If you start big, your project may start to look like Great-

Grandma's cedar chest on the Oregon Trail—very desirable in North Dakota, but abandoned somewhere in the Rocky Mountains of Wyoming. If you start small, then you make your mistakes on a small scale, and you will learn a great deal. You will find out what kind of care the plants need, how long they take to grow, and how much medicine they yield. If it all works out OK, and you think you can handle more, then you can scale up with confidence.

Choose plants that are appropriate to your bioregion, including heirloom species that have been successfully cultivated in your area over time, as well as medicinals that are native to the local wild lands. Hops (*Humulus lupulus*), in days gone by, were a significant cash crop in my area. Spikenard (*Aralia californica*) grows wild on the creek just below the seed house. So, when I started working this land, I planted both hops and spikenard, and they remain among the most trouble-free and productive of all the plants that we grow.

Plants gravitate to their preferred habitat. Take elecampane (*Inula helenium*), for instance. Some years back when the kids were little, having expanded our medicinal garden to about a hundred species, we were actively benefiting by living in the midst of plant diversity. We watched the interplay of butterflies and blossoms, listened to the buzz of myriad native pollinators on the fennel, ate burdock (*Arctium lappa*) roots for dinner, and dried the elecampane roots to make tea for alleviating the inevitable coughs of the cold season ahead.

Throughout that summer we worked happily, cultivating between the plants and spreading composted manure from the goat barn, while watching the elecampane offer up its sunny blossoms to the Southern Oregon sun. Being seed-savers, when the ray flowers shriveled in the drying breezes of August, we were soon busy collecting the seed-laden pappus. According to our usual practices, we did not collect all of the seed—we left some for the goldfinches, and some blew away.

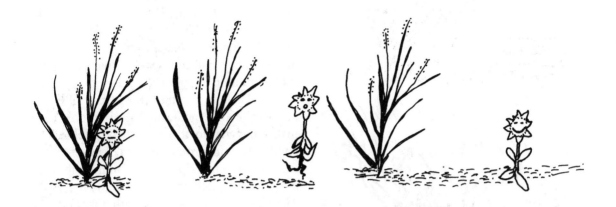

The next spring, I noticed a familiar seedling emerging in the fertile soil next to the foundation of our yurt. The seedling was partly shaded by the yurt. It looked like an elecampane. The plant grew enormously, with leaves and flowers much larger than those growing in the full sun, producing in time a root of magnificent proportions. One of the main principles of natural gardening techniques had been clearly elucidated—the plants know best where to grow and, given the right conditions, they will eventually gravitate there—humans or no.

By watching the plants from season to season, we can learn where they prefer to grow and guide them toward naturalization. To the degree that plants are successfully naturalized, they require correspondingly less human input, while remaining available for food or medicine as circumstances require.

Perhaps the "hands-on" way of relating to plants in cultivation might benefit from occasional periods of "hands-off," giving plants the space they need to demonstrate their own wisdom through self-regeneration and relocation. In this case, all us gardeners need to do is sit back and watch to determine where our next efforts will be most fruitful. I think you'll be glad to hear that too much weeding is contraindicated, lest we interrupt those patterns of natural regeneration.

My advice to gardeners is to let at least a few of each kind of plant go unharvested— let them go to seed. To observe these plants completing their cycles on the farm will give valuable insight into how your gardening can merge with nature. This is a piece of the plant wisdom that keeps the earth green.

Keep the cycles close to home. Everywhere in nature, there are cycles and circles. The moon soars through the night skies, the dew falls, the sun appears, the dew goes up to the clouds, and later the rain comes down. Learning to recognize the cyclic nature of the movement of natural resources (minerals, carbon, nitrogen, water) on the land and learning to input human activities in a way to keep these cycles strong and close to home will make your gardening more energy efficient. Your labor will give maximum returns, and you will spend less money.

The carbon cycle. When I pull weeds by hand, I often keep the tall weeds (such as pigweed, wild lettuce, and thistles) in a pile and, when the pile gets big and juicy, throw it over the fence to the questing noses of my goats. They consume everything except the roots, grunting in approval. Later, they poop.

Usually around the first rains of autumn, feeling medieval, I gird my loins and make my way to the goat shed, pitchfork in hand. The loin girding consists of me checking to make sure my zipper is up on my bib overalls, and the pitchfork, of course, is my lance. The goats are fair damsels, with noses pressed up against the fence, waving multicolored handkerchiefs and calling out "Halloo, Halloo, look at me!"

I do not know why the goats are so interested in the process of cleaning out the shed, but they inevitably get right in the way as I pitch the hay and manure out of the open shed onto the pile outdoors. Working with my (im)patience, I set down my tool for a minute, go out the gate, collect a shirt-full of windfall apples, and dump these over the fence, far from the shed. If I do not cut the apples in half, it takes the goats a long time to eat them. This is because goats, for some reason, were originally given less than a full complement of teeth. Consequently, they have to gum the apples for a long time before the juicy orbs get sized down to chewability.

The water cycle. Where does your water come from and where does it go? If you are in a high rain area and can rely on natural rainfall for watering your crops, this is incredibly fortunate. Rain water is not empty—it contains nitrogen and is energetically stimulating to plants. If you have a river, creek, or pond on your land, then in most cases this surface water is better for your medicinals than water that comes from a well. Clean surface water will probably be warmer (which is good, because warm water is less shocking to the plants) and will certainly contain more nutrients than the well water.

The water goes on the land and into the plants, to be capillaried back into the water table or evaporated or transpired back up into the atmosphere to form rain clouds (sometime, somewhere). Truly, the rain is both as new as the dew and as old as the steamy birth of life on earth.

Now I can pitch for awhile without skewering any curious goats. I'm building a reasonable mix of carbon (hay) and nitrogen (manure). Given some rain followed by a few bright autumn days, it won't be long before the pile begins to compost. A thin waft of steam will rise in the morning mist as the pile shoulders down. Bacteria are doing their work, making all the ingredients into bioavailable humus. Earthworms are working their way up out of the ground into the pile, further digesting all the ingredients. They warm their tails on the periphery.

After the first cook-down, I turn the pile again, tossing the ingredients further from the shed, closer to the gate. The pile heats up again. After a few weeks, I have finished compost, located near the gate where I can come get it with a wheelbarrow. Local hay and farm-derived weeds have been converted into the perfect nutrient. The tight cycle is complete when the compost is spread back out to the field, nurturing medicinal herbs.

Whenever possible, direct-seed during the appropriate season instead of starting plants in the greenhouse and transplanting. Plants that are direct-seeded will naturalize more quickly and develop a strong root system, which is the foundation of plant health. For instance, this year I started giant Zanzibar castor (*Ricinus communis zanzibariensis*) plants in gallon pots in the greenhouse and when I transplanted them out to the garden, took the precaution of pushing more seed into the hills around the transplants. The transplanted castors sputtered a bit, but eventually dug in and started to grow. Meanwhile, the extra seeds germinated volcanically, quickly making large and vigorous seedlings.

Within the first month, it became obvious that the direct-seeded plants were out-shining the transplants, so I callously pulled out the transplants. By late August, the direct-seeded plants reached full glory and started setting seed of their own. Turns out, I needn't have bothered with the greenhouse at all!

Hold onto your flats! Although the "germination time" for most seeds is widely reported, both in reference books and in seed catalogs, these are really only estimations based on germinating the seeds under a certain set of conditions. If seeds do not emerge when expected, then either they have rotted or they are still alive in the soil. I've found that many gardeners just shrug their shoulders at this point, toss the flat, and go on to something more interesting.

A more proactive approach, especially with tropical and other large seeded plants, is to dig up a number of seeds and give them an examination. If they are rotten, then by all means recycle the flat! If they are still plump and alive, then they will eventually sprout. The variables of time, temperature, light, moisture, drainage, day-length, moon-cycle, and season are all factors that contribute to the germination response. The makeup of the potting soil, and bacterial and fungal activity within the potting soil, also has a profound influence on seed germination. Learning to differentiate flats of dead seeds from flats of live seeds is really important.

Make sure to thin plants to the appropriate spacing. Although it seems hard-hearted to pull out all those little seedlings, making sure that plants have room to grow to their full size without competing with their neighbors will increase plant health and yield very noticeably. I first became aware of this phenomenon when planting garlic—plants left too closely together in the row made single bulbs, while plants given plenty of room produced large rosettes. Within reason, the more room you give the plants, the bigger the yield.

Cultivate often around the crown of the plant. If your hands are tough enough, just use your fingers. Remove the weeds and fluff up the soil around the plant. This applies both to plants in the garden and potted plants. In fact, the weeds that sprout up around plants are our friends, because they encourage us to cultivate the soil. This helps the roots of the plant to breathe, increases water absorption, and improves bioavailability of nutrients. Plants love this attention. Within minutes, the human will be humming, the humus will be humming, the plants will be humming, and the hummingbirds will be humming. A good gardener doesn't need to differentiate between all these hums.

Dress with organic compost or rotted manure around the crown of the plant, especially if the plant is unhealthy looking, yellowing, or not developing quickly enough. Work the compost in with your fingers. Compost is well-tolerated by almost all plants and slowly releases mellow nutrients, thereby increasing the nutritional content of foods and the medicinal activity of herbs. Of course, the forest medicinals, for the most part, do not do well with any fertilization, but most other plants respond very well to this treatment. When a plant is suffering, adding compost is often the answer to setting things right.

Plant in triangles. The geometric figure known as the triangle is a naturally stable form, and gardeners can invoke this stability by planting in multiples of three. Planting out in the shape of a triangle maximizes the space available to each plant, in both the root zone and the aerial parts. Planting in triangles optimizes the availability of water, nutrients, and light for efficient branching, flowering, and bearing seeds. Planting in triangles also improves wind resistance.

One trick I often use, when plants begin to mature and set heavy seed crops, is to tie them together at the top (into a tripod of sorts) with string. This keeps them from lodging (blowing over in the wind) and keeps the precious seed crop elevated from the moist ground. This practice results in clean, hard seed that is fully ripened before collection, with a concomitant increase in seed longevity, germination, and vigor. I often use this trick with poppies (*Papaver* spp.), as the heavy capsules tend to weigh down the willowy plants.

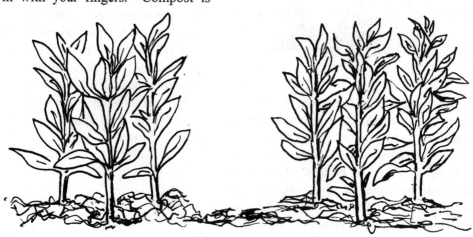

Use naturally occurring seedlings. Why go through the trouble of planting seed in the greenhouse, if perfectly acclimatized seedlings can be found in the vicinity of the mother plant? Such seedlings are free for the taking, their root systems are naturally shaped, and they are preselected by the rigors of outdoor living (in other words, poorly adapted seedlings have died away, giving space to more robust individuals). Volunteer seedlings may be transplanted back to pots or out to the field. They make better plants than greenhouse-grown seedlings. One of the plants I usually propagate from naturally occurring seedlings is angelica, which volunteers easily but can be difficult to start intentionally.

Select for vigor. The gardener will do well to choose the most robust seedlings as the ones to keep and nourish into adulthood. Seedlings that seem stressed, undersized, or are spaced too closely together are best thinned out and removed from the gene pool. Over several generations, this practice will produce a productive strain of plants that are resistant to disease and are resilient in the face of environmental stress.

Rogue out the undesirables. As a plant grows and matures, it develops individual traits that give you clues as to how productive and useful the plant will be at harvest. The size and shape of the plant, the color and aroma of the leaves, the quality of the flowers and fruits, and the general liveliness of the plant are all significant factors. If any of these attributes seem sub-

standard, or if the plant appears diseased or unduly vulnerable to insect damage, then it is a good idea to pull up the plant and lay it down in the compost pile. The garden space is better used by plants that more accurately fit your concept of what constitutes a good plant. Furthermore, if you intend to save seed from your plants, and since both positive and negative traits can be inherited, then you want your parent plants to be of the highest quality, producing good food and medicine.

Pay attention to timing. The potting soil is made with the very best ingredients, compiled and combined with the utmost of care. The seed you are using is from the recent harvest, and has been stored in cool, dry conditions to preserve its integrity. Your planting technique is beyond reproach—you sprinkle the seed on the surface of the soil, barely cover it with a little more soil, tamp it securely, and keep it watered, warm, and in the light. You even utter a few prayers of encouragement to the little seeds, willing them to swell and break dormancy. And still, the seeds do not come up!

There is only one variable that you have not controlled, and over which you may have little control. That variable is *time,* that most powerful of entities, which witnesses the birth and death of civilizations, and erodes mountains into sand. We humans strive for efficiency, but it is through patience that great deeds are accomplished. And so it is with planting seeds. Seeds sown at the wrong time of year may be seeds sown in vain. And seeds sown with the expectation of quick results may become seeds thrown prematurely to their ruin.

So, let us not assess time on our paltry human terms, but rather let time take its course, and stand ready to reap the advantage of patience. Here, again, diversity comes to our rescue. If we sow seeds appropriate to the season, and we sow many kinds of seeds at every season, then success will follow on the heels of success. All we need to do is to keep a watchful eye for the results, and rejoice at every germination.

Sonic effects. The frogs are the canary in the cage. If they look good (which pretty much comes down to four legs and two eyes on each frog, no more and no less) then it means that the ecosystem is probably in good shape. Frogs are sensitive little creatures, and if they don't look right, it's a sign that something really *isn't* right. So we build habitat, such as piles of carbonaceous debris, ponds, and wetlands in order to encourage the little guys to stay around. Frogs are part of a balanced ecosystem and they are really, really cute.

Frogs tune up in the summer evenings, blowing out the skin underneath their little chins and creating a noise much louder than such a small creature ought to be able to make. Certainly the bagpipe was created in more modern times than the froggy croaker, but the concept is the same and the results are equally, well, impossible to ignore! Plants love the croaking of frogs. It stimulates their *stomata* to open at night, to transpire and breathe. Frog music is Beethoven to beans.

Frog song is also a clear signal that spring has indeed arrived. For those farmers who are eagerly waiting to plant seeds, but don't want to "start too early," the frogs can be a sure signal of the right window for early planting. Winter nights are relatively quiet and cold, but when you awake at four o'clock in the morning to a raucous frog party, you know that the water is warm enough to grow froggy eggs. Therefore, the dirt is warm enough for planting peas.

Cricket music effects plants in a similar way, as does your voice as you talk and sing to your plants. Plants are nonjudgmental. They appreciate us even if our songs are not always on key. They want us nearby even though sometimes we make a wrong step. The relationship is well-summarized by a trailside sign I came across in Kunming, "Flower is smiling to you, please take care of her growing."

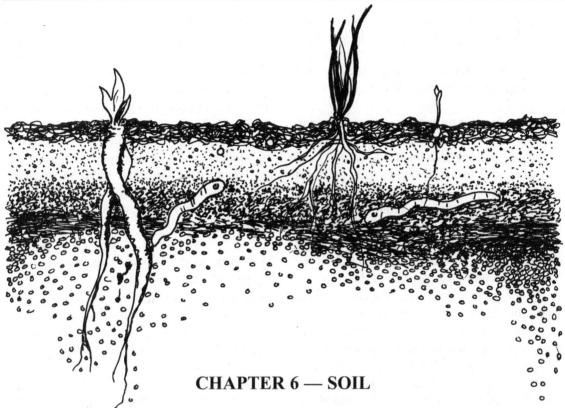

CHAPTER 6 — SOIL

Dirt first. Earthworms nourish the soil so plants can thrive. Perhaps it is not an accident that when the plants die, they make more food for the earthworms. This is a ground-level symbiotic cycle that occurs throughout the warm months, both in the wilds and in the carefully tended organic garden. Indeed, without the mixing and aeration accomplished by the lowly earthworm, our soils would be airless and, as a consequence, lifeless. Since it is the soil that nourishes the crops that feed our bodies, there is a vital link between soil health and human health. Therefore, it is a core principle of natural gardening techniques that we feed the soil and trust that the soil will feed the crops that feed us. It is a strange twist of fate that we owe our health to the worms!

What is soil? Soil is an admixture of living organisms, minerals, and humus. Organisms that live in and on the soil range in size from unicellular bacteria, algae, fungi, and protozoa to the visible creatures: earthworms, insects, vertebrates, and plants. The primary producers of easily assimilated carbon and nitrogen are the photosynthetic bacteria, algae, moss, lichens, and plants. When these organisms die, they feed the secondary producers: the aerobic bacteria, fungi, and earthworms. As all these organisms interact with each other (birthing, eating, excreting, and dying), they convert carbon into organic nutrients that feed the plants.

When bedrock breaks down into gravel, sand, silt, and clay, mineral soil is created. Sand and gravel are coarse particles that allow water to drain down through the soil. Silt and clay are composed of very small (colloidal) particles that hold onto water. Mineral soils are generally alkaline in nature and they provide mineral nutrients (such as phosphorus) to plants.

Organic matter in soil is composed of living organisms and humus. When dead plant and animal matter decomposes to the point where it is no longer subject to rapid change, it becomes humus. Humus is fluffy and light, acting like a sponge to absorb water and, when the water drains away, to hold air. Humus binds the soil together. Humus is generally acid in nature and provides carbon and nitrogen to plants. Humus is also the site of much biological activity (in other words, life).

How soils form in nature. In nature, soils form in layers from the top down. For instance, even wind and water deposited soils (e.g. loess and alluvium) occur in layers with the most recent stratum at the surface. Prairie soils are formed by the yearly growth and deterioration of a large biomass of grasses and forbs. Here, along with worms, bacteria are the primary decomposers. The deep, black top soil of the Midwestern states was formed in this way.

Woodland soils are formed by the yearly breakdown of leaves and woody debris from trees. In the woods, fungi (not bacteria) are the primary decomposers. Woodland soils are distinctly layered. On the surface, you find a thick mulch of dead leaves. Pushing aside this stratum, you can see the decomposition layer where woody debris is converted into humus. The spongy, white matrix of fungal mycelia is often quite evident in this layer. Below this you find (usually) mineral soil mixed with loam, sand, gravel, and clay, all bound together by humus. Successful medicinal herb growers learn to mimic these wild systems in domestic culture

Note that in these natural soil-generating systems (the prairie and the forest) the healthy growth of wild plants occurs without added fertilizer. Most vegetable gardeners cannot grow their crops without using fertilizer of some sort. However, vegetables are cultigens— they exist *because* of people, and, over centuries of selection, these plants have developed dependency on fertilizer. On the other hand, most medicinal herbs remain unchanged from their wild ancestors. If such herbs are grown as part of a balanced ecosystem (in the forest or as part of a rotation of cover crops), then they can be successfully grown without adding any compost or manure at all.

Cover-cropping with leguminous plants, such as clover, peas, and fava beans, infuses the soil with sufficient nitrogen to support the growth of most herbs. Additional nitrogen may derive from manure deposited by domestic stock and from the droppings of birds feeding on berries in the shelterbelt. When plants make dark green leaves, this is an indication of sufficient nitrogen in the soil. If leaves begin to turn yellow, then either the plant is going dormant, there is not enough nitrogen in the soil (add compost), or there is insufficient drainage (the roots are drowning).

Mulching promotes worms and improves the ability of the soil to retain rain water. Mulching supports plants in their preference for layered soils. Compost, rice hulls, straw, coir, or any other kind of carbon-rich material can be layered on the surface around perennial plants and trees to rejuvenate them. This is a harmless method of promoting moisture, controlling weeds, and maintaining fertility in the garden of medicinal herbs.

Planning ahead. In this age of instant gratification, it is difficult for us to think much ahead of ourselves. In gardening, if we think ahead just a few seasons, we can gradually begin the process of making soil that will sustain us for years. So we work first at building soil and then, when the soil is ready, the soil grows the plants.

CHAPTER 7 — SEEDS

Have faith in seeds story. The sagging milk carton, with its precious cargo of dirt and seeds, clutched in both hands and held protectively to my chest, barely survived intact the six-block journey from Lincoln grade school to our stucco house at 406 Magowan Avenue in Iowa City. Surely, it is a sign of great love when our mothers allow us to place such travel-worn, leaky vessels on the windowsill, where light washes in over the porcelain of a kitchen sink, otherwise scrupulously scrubbed clean of anything resembling soil.

Miss McLaughlin, my plump and matronly kindergarten teacher, had wisely chosen the lowly (although to most kindergarteners inedible) radish as a fast and infallible germinator, in order to introduce her noisy, elbowing, poking, whispering, and giggling charges to the quiet miracle of germination. I tamped the disrupted surface of the soil in my waxy milk carton, watered again, and watched in awe a few days later as the fat cotyledons rose up quickly from the dark dirt. My radishes grew; I watered and watched over them and had no requirements of them. I wished to be friends with them. They soon tumbled over the sides of the container in etiolated glory. I never ate them.

This early success gave way to other trials—I prepared another milk carton and planted one of the brown, teardrop-shaped seeds extracted from an apple core and, by its side, one of the slick, tough-membraned seeds of an orange. "Those seeds won't grow," said my older and wiser brother, his arms folded across his chest. He knew that proper seeds came from a seed packet, not from fruits in a kitchen. My big sister, with a shake of her blonde pigtails, asserted, "Oranges don't grow in Iowa."

Always the optimist, I watered and waited (a long time, as I recall), daily climbing up on the counter and craning my neck toward the back of the sink. Eventually, my attention wavered and the container dried somewhat, but evidently this was just what was needed. One Sunday morning, I again checked the crumbling milk carton, and my squeal of delight brought both brother and sister (all sageness and dignity forgotten) tripping over each other, running from the next room. I can still see the way their jaws dropped when I pointed out the unlikely spectacle—the two seedlings emerging in cadence, side by side. The identity of the seedlings was clearly defined by their seed coats borne up like shining helmets, soon thrown off as the leaves unfolded to the light.

This experience engendered in my inner being an undying faith in seeds. I learned that if I created the right conditions of sun, soil, and water and planted the seeds carefully, just beneath the surface, tamped them in firmly, and kept them evenly moist, then eventually I would surely be rewarded. I never forgot these early successes, and never lost the excitement felt when seedlings push through the dark earth.

Of course, my brother and sister were right, in a way. Oranges and apples are not usually grown from seed, and my little seedlings never amounted to much. For all of us, experiments like this yield information, and this is one way that we progress in our knowledge. Besides, planting seeds was so much fun that I could not stop.

Advantages of cultivating from seed. After a lifetime of propagating plants, I have found that cultivating from seed is the most useful and effective method. Plants grown from seed produce a robust root structure. In general, seed-grown plants are better than those produced by cuttings, because plants grown from seed produce more entire and deeply seated roots and are thus more resistant to crown rot. Seed-grown plants demonstrate improved vigor, stature, yield, and longevity. Growing from seed also improves genetic diversity, as each individual is genetically distinct, unlike plants grown from cuttings, which are clones. Therefore, plants grown from seed will give a diverse population, demonstrating resilience in the face of environmental challenges and more likely to accommodate (sometimes over the course of several generations) to conditions in the domestic garden.

Variations in seed sowing strategies. The ideal technique for successfully sowing seeds varies according to the species being planted. Some large seeds, such as nasturtiums, are best sown very deeply. However, peas are large, too, and they do best when sown very shallowly. Plants in the *Lobelia* family produce very tiny seeds that are best strewn on the surface of the soil. *Artemisia* species do best when germinated in the light, while celandine germinates best in the shade. Some seeds, such as pagoda tree, have a very hard seed coat (testa) and must absolutely be nicked with a knife or rubbed on sandpaper before planting. Others, such as curry leaf tree, have no testa at all. In this case, the challenge is to keep the seed from dehydrating, and therefore the seed does not withstand dry storage and must be sown immediately when ripe.

Rates of germination response. Some seeds, such as carob tree, germinate quickly in warm soil; others, such as ginseng, germinate slowly in cool soil. Some seeds, such as many in the lily family, require the passage of several seasons before germination is possible. They demonstrate double-dormancy, germinating usually in the spring of the second year. Two-phase germinators are plants that make a root in the first year and aerial parts in the second year. Trillium seeds exhibit both double-dormancy and two-phase germination, so it is not unusual for them to show their first leaf in the spring of the third year.

Longevity of seeds. Some seeds germinate best when they are very recent, such as coltsfoot and valerian, which have short-lived seed. Others give their highest germination after being aged for a year or more, such as cucumber and Hopi tobacco.

Many seeds are capable of remaining viable for extended periods of time. Experiments at the Michigan Agricultural College that began in the fall of 1885 have demonstrated that dry-stored seeds of evening primrose and yellow dock can remain viable for up to 80 years. Seeds of mullein can lie dormant in the ground for decades and germinate joyfully as soon as the soil is tilled and the sunlight awakens them. Seeds of the lotus (*Nelumbo nucifera*) have been shown to give 100% germination after 237 years of storage in moist peat.

The importance of rhizobia. Seeds of plants with highly nodulated roots, such as: beans, bundle flower, clover, and indigos, germinate and grow most vigorously in soils where the nitrogen-fixing soil bacteria known as rhizobia are active. Soils that have been previously cover-cropped are sure to be already teeming with rhizobia. However, if seeds of this sort are to be sown in new potting soil or in a garden where legumes have not previously been grown, then it makes sense to pre-inoculate the seed. Rhizobium inoculant is commonly available through nurseries and seed companies. Inoculating the seed before planting will create the proper conditions for rhizobial symbiosis, which mutually benefits both fungus and plant.

Gibberellic acid dependency. Seeds of certain plants will germinate and grow best in a medium where high concentrations of the plant hormone gibberellic acid are present. Since this growth hormone is produced by the breakdown of fungi in the soil, then it is very important to use decomposed leaves or woody debris in the potting soil when planting these seeds. Bloodroot, datura, pulsatilla, and butcher's broom are examples of plants that require an extra helping of gibberellic acid before germination is possible.

Unlocking the secrets of germination is one of the most challenging, yet rewarding, tasks that a seedsperson can engage. Gaining an understanding of the personal needs of each plant is usually knowledge bought with years of hard work—mainly "tions," like cogitation, experimentation, and observation. Then again, as the following two stories illustrate, the best methodology is sometimes discovered through serendipitous circumstances.

Stories of serendipity. More than once, I tried growing skunk cabbage by planting the newly harvested seeds in moist flats in the shade-house. I never got very good results—a sprout or two after a year or two was the best I could expect. Then, I stashed some skunk cabbage seed in a plastic bag of moist coir in the fridge and left it (then forgot it) on a low shelf for a good two years. This reveals how often I clean the refrigerator! Eventually, I rediscovered the bag, now a plasticized lump of mold, and thinking that I would compost it later, tossed it into an open box in the seed room. There it sat, at 60° F in the dark, for a couple more weeks. One morning, as the light from the one northern window filtered into the seed room and illuminated the box, an out-of-place greenness caught my eye. It was the developing leaves of the skunk cabbage seeds, transformed into pointy-leaved seedlings, trying to pierce their way out of the bag! I could only conclude that the long period of anaerobic curing, despite the presence of mold, was just what was needed to develop the embryo to the point where full germination was possible!

Another time I was experimenting with planting coriander in trays in the greenhouse at different times of year, trying to discover when best to sow it for optimal germination. One of these attempts was made in the late summer, and the seeds simply refused to germinate. After awhile I concluded that the seed was dead, and with disgust threw all the soil from the barren tray out onto the compost pile. A few cool nights and bright days went by, and one morning, in passing the compost pile, I noticed a green fuzz. On closer inspection, I discovered that this was composed of hundreds of beautiful coriander seedlings germinating in unison, their pointy leaves lifted jauntily to the sun. "Well," I mused. "Next time I'll direct-seed the coriander!"

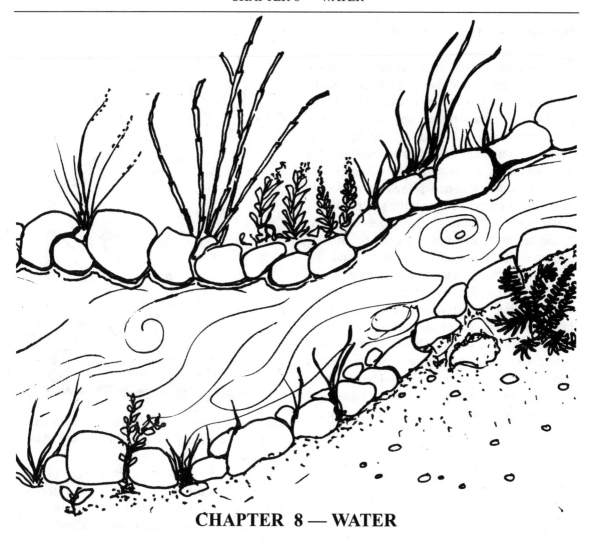

CHAPTER 8 — WATER

Rain. Right now, as I write this, the rain is thrumming hard on the roof of the seed house. It was raining yesterday, too, and the day before. Leaks we never knew we had have turned up in the porch, and there's a rivulet running under the front door. Outside, above the glistening roof of the seed house, there have been intermittent rainbows. Under the ground, the water table is rising. The creek is at full capacity, boiling between its banks in a headlong rush to the ocean.

This kind of cleanout is good for the health of the creek, and I'm pretty excited about our new skinny dipping hole that's being dug out right now. I think the salmon will like it, too. Actually, there's no backhoe involved, as nature is doing the work. Cleaning up wind-damaged trees this fall, my son and I built a baffle across the creek with logs and fallen branches. Now, the rising waters of the creek are pouring over this baffle and digging out a deep depression on the downstream side. By summer, this will have become a beautiful green pool. We're blessed with water, but despite this abundance, I never, for a moment, think of water as being ordinary.

Deep within the ground, miraculously, there is water. This subterranean aquifer, filtered clean by running through the capillaries of the earth, is really a fossil resource that must be used sparingly so it can continue to be used by all. We recognize that water is the most valuable substance on earth, and we do everything in our power to keep it around.

HOLD ONTO THAT WATER!

Water features. Here on our little farm, we've designed a few water features that store water for later use. Now, in the winter, our outdoor pond is rain fed and full to capacity. Our pond in the greenhouse is full, too. Locating a small pond and fountain inside the greenhouse not only serves as a convenient source of warm water for watering in transplants, but it encourages frogs to hop throughout the greenhouse, a major advantage in maintaining overall greenhouse health. The barrel that I use for mixing comfrey tea is full to overflowing, and the goat's water trough, located under the eaves of the goat shed, is full to the brim.

While subterranean water is best for humans to drink, the plants prefer to drink rain water or surface water. This kind of water is better for plants. Therefore, when gardeners and farmers are looking for a land base, access to irrigation from rivers, streams, lakes, and ponds is one of the main factors to consider.

City folks do well to collect rain to water their plants. Install a barrel under the downspout, and keep it covered to keep mosquitoes out. If collecting rain is impractical and the only water source is chlorinated city water, then steps can be taken to improve the situation. A small pond, barrel, or cistern can be used as a holding tank, allowing the chlorine time to gas off, eventually converting city water to water that the plants will recognize and love—water alive with bacteria. To avoid stagnation, it really helps to aerate the water by some means, such as: daily stirring, adding in new water from a height, or by installing a fountain.

When to water. Regardless of the water source, it is an important adage of natural gardening techniques that irrigation is done in the late afternoon and at night (or if fungal diseases are likely to be a problem, then in the early morning). Not only does this stretch the water by limiting evaporation, but it tunes into

the daily growth pattern of plants, where water is absorbed during the cool hours, and photosynthesis is initiated when sunlight hits.

Cover crops keep the drying rays of the sun off of the soil, and they hold water like a sponge. Moist soil is live soil, thriving with bacteria, fungi, and earthworms. Keeping the earth covered from the drying rays of the sun is the best way to maintain healthy soil. A cover crop of oats and peas is probably the most hydrophilic choice for a winter cover crop, and buckwheat is probably the most water conserving cover crop for summer use.

Using coir for water retention. Mulches are commonly employed for keeping the soil moist and lively. Coir (also known as coco-peat) is one of the best substances to use for mulch. Coir is made of ground up pith from the pericarp of the coconut. It comes from the tropics, where there is biomass to spare, and it arrives here in compressed blocks. On our farm, the dry coir is stored in the goat shed. One day, returning in the rain from my goat feeding chores, I took the opportunity to haul a generous number of these blocks of coir out to the comfrey bed. I then laid them out on the soil surface. It was raining. Over the next few days, the coir blocks absorbed the rain. The coir swelled up, turned a rich red color, and expanded mightily in volume. I spread the moist, spongy coir thickly over the beds, smothering the weeds. Come spring, the comfrey will grow through the coir mulch. Given the hydrophilic nature of the coir, we probably won't have to water the comfrey until summer, and we won't have to weed it—ever!

Using pumice to increase drainage. Out in the field, the newly planted poppies (*Papaver somniferum*) are raising their first tiny leaves to the rain. Even though they make their best flowers and seed during the dryness of summer, poppies love to germinate and grow during the winter's cold and wet. These nascent poppies won't float away, either, because they were planted by first laying down a layer of compost, then covering the compost with a generous layer of horticultural pumice, and finally sprinkling the poppy seeds on top of the pumice. When it rains, the seeds migrate down to the compost where they germinate. The aerial parts then grow up through the pumice toward the light, resulting in a plant that is protected from crown rot, deeply rooted, and securely buttressed against heavy wind.

We employ various techniques to hold onto this precious water: increasing the holding capacity of our creek, filling all human-made ponds and cisterns, mulching around the perennials, and growing cover crops and medicinal herbs that hold water in their tissues. At night, I lie on my back in bed and listen to the rain thrumming on the roof, and the plop, plop as the leaky roof drips into a pan in the laundry room. Every once in a while a trickle of water makes its way down the chimney and sizzles when it contacts the hot surface of the woodstove. Eyes tightly shut, I smile, fold my hands over my chest, and stretch out my toes. The rain is good.

Illustration. Method of coiling garden hose in order to limit formation of kinks or knots. Is it an accident that this also creates the symbol for infinity?

CHAPTER 9 — SUN

Planting corn story. These days on my farm, even in the summer, the quiet spells between bouts of rototilling stretch longer and longer—not only because I try to avoid tillage as a rule, but because the tiller is getting so old and cranky that it's a real challenge to get it started! I have to remember to turn up the throttle and turn the key to "start," after which ends the practical part and begins the dance: run around the tiller three times counterclockwise; check the wind direction with wetted finger; turn the choke on, off, then on again; whip myself in the forehead with the starter rope; fix the jumper cables; look at the sun; cross two fingers behind my back; and act like I don't care. When the engine actually catches, it's such a surprise that I have been known to fall over backwards, starter rope in hand, right into the dandelions.

On this particular day, I needed the tiller, because the soil in my proposed corn-field had truly warmed up, and I was ready to have some fun planting corn and beans. The tines bit feebly through the mowed remains of the red clover cover crop, down into the dark earth. The rusted remains of the exhaust unit on the side of the tiller clattered and bounced, held on by one tattered bolt. I sighed. It would require many passes to prepare the soil to sufficient depth.

Crows watched from the shadows of the big oak tree in the gathering heat as I toiled back and forth. For me, tilling is an iconic task that puts me in touch with the long lineage of earth tillers, the farmers who, over the ages, have fed the people. Somewhere in Czechoslovakia, a potato farmer bore the seed of my blood generations before my baby buttocks ever saw the light of sun. So involved did I become in reflecting on the history of agriculture, that I took little notice of the task at hand. The crows ruffled their feathers again and I ran the tiller down the row for the last time, up onto the grass by the driveway, and, blessed moment of silence, turned the key to "off."

Using the hoe, I scribed seven long, deep furrows in the newly tilled field. Stepping back to observe my handiwork, I noticed without surprise that the rows were not really straight, rather slightly sinuous, although practically parallel, like a family of petroglyphic rattlesnakes on the roof of an Anasazi cave. I counted them again—yes, seven.

Using the long-handled shovel and wheelbarrow, I then moved composted goat manure from the pile out by the goat shed, wheeled it along the driveway to the field, and generously filled the bottom of each furrow with lovely black compost. "No reason to fertilize the weeds," I thought, "I'll band the compost under the row." This process took up until lunchtime and I considered taking a break, but then thought better of it. For me, planting corn is a holy act, and so fasting felt right. Besides, after all that preparatory work, I was excited to sow some seeds!

I took off my t-shirt and my boots, leaving them in a sweaty little heap next to the tiller. The sun warmed my back as again I walked down the rows, using my bare feet, pushing a little fine dirt in on top of the compost. "We want those seeds to sprout," I said to the crows, "not rot."

The seed room was dark and cold as I rummaged about in the vegetable seed barrel. This year, it would be sweet red corn interspersed with scarlet runner beans. It's a classic combo, really, another little symbiotic cycle there in the field, beans fixing atmospheric nitrogen for the corn, corn creating a trellis for the beans. You might say, "Hey, I thought this was about growing medicinal herbs!" To which I'd reply that sweet red corn is full of antioxidant anthocyanins and consumption of fresh corn-on-the-cob in season helps prevent colon cancer. The flowers of scarlet runner beans are crunchily edible and the dried pods are a valuable diuretic used in treating urinary infection. Truly, hand-grown food is the foundation of health— ultimately there is no difference between food and medicine.

Tuning up before planting seeds. Back out in the field with bags of seed in hand, my excitement mounted. Soon, very soon, I would drop seeds in soil. Standing at the beginning of the field, I closed my eyes and expanded my breast to the sun, a seed bag in each hand. I felt the position of the sun, and the position of my fleeting furrows on the land. This is a little hard to describe, but it is something central to natural gardening techniques. For lack of a better term, I call it "tuning." Whether defining a garden path, building a greenhouse, or planning a new asparagus bed, you take a moment to feel the energy of the land, to make sure that these changes resonate well with the availability of water and the movement of people, materials, crops, and especially that giver of energy, the sun. If it doesn't feel right, then you fine-tune until it resonates. When you care this much about the land, it glows.

This method of tuning is something I do before I pray. Now, I'm not Native American and so have no cultural heritage of ceremony for the planting of corn and beans, crops that originated here in the new world and are held sacred by the First Nations people. So, I simply bathed the seeds in good intention and prayed from the heart that they would feed people well and cure all ills of body and soul.

Sowing the corn seeds. Then I got on with the fun part. Resisting the temptation to plant too many seeds, I dropped them one by one, first a few corn seeds, then a bean, then more corn seeds. The red corn was so red, a fiery kernel against the black earth. The beans were so smooth in my fingers, so heavy and cosmic, purple and shiny, shot through with a constellation of pink—three for the crows, one for me.

In my imagination the corn crackled out of the ground behind me, and the beans lifted their fat cotyledons to the sun, tendriling their way up the cornstalks. The seeds lasted to the end of the final furrow. Starting over again at the beginning, I dropped to my knees and crawled back over the field one last time, pushing the soil from the edges of the furrow back on top of the seeds and patting it down by hand. The work was hard, the sun burned down, and I could feel my temples pulsing with each beat of my heart. Sweat trickled out of my hair, down my forehead, and off the end of my nose. I noticed that dirt was sticking to the backs of my hands, glued there by sweat, the arm hairs rising up like a field of wheat. I was so happy, I was singing. A crow swooped over the field, and I looked up, sweat stinging my eyes, and said, "Not yet."

Having crawled the whole field over, I stood a bit shakily and rubbed the crust of soil from my knees. "Grow baby grow," I mentally intoned for the hundredth time. Then I said out loud, "I just love this!" and went in for lunch.

CHAPTER 10 — TREES

The new homestead story. When we first moved to our new place, in the front yard of the house grew mainly star thistle *(Centaurea solstitialis)* which around here is a sign of abused land. It was a tough, nasty, and spiny patch of thistle, sporting a gnarly centerpiece composed of a large dead stump overshadowing a sickly (and not very kid-friendly) prickly pear cactus. Around the perimeter ran a dirt track where the previous occupants had raced their all terrain vehicles (ATV's). We began the rehabilitation effort by pulling star thistle until our fingers and thumbs were stained green. Then we dug out the dead stump and rolled it off to the side, and finally prodded the cactus out of its spot and tipped it over the edge of the creek bank to skeletonize in the shade. It went roots up and soon melted into the dirt.

We took out the larger rocks from the yard, tilled all around the house, scattered some chicken manure, tilled again, and then planted red clover, which soon germinated and grew to become a thick green carpet. The children could now run barefoot! This was also a good start for future beds of herbs and garden

vegetables. Then, in order to keep cars from driving on the lawn, we planted a cedar of Lebanon *(Cedrus libani)* smack dab where the entrance to the old ATV track had been. I had private reservations as to whether this true cedar from far away would grow well in the compacted soil, but was pleasantly surprised to find that the handsome evergreen truly loved this spot, showing signs of quick growth during the cool weather of spring and again in the autumn.

The goat variable. We had goats at the time (lots of them) and they were allowed a quarter acre spot near the road for their goat shed and pasture. Goats are browsers and in order to be healthy they really need roughage in their diet. This we normally supplied by tossing them the weeds we'd pulled from the garden (although they wouldn't touch the star thistle), as well as green trimmings removed from various trees and thrown over the fence to them. The goats would come running, pull the leaves off the branches with their rough tongues, then chew the bark right down to the bright wood. If we didn't throw in new branches quickly enough, they'd eat some of the wood, too! We kept the goats in their enclosure, because allowed to roam free they were like the plague of Mordor—moving across the land, devouring trees in their path.

The summer sun bore down and Joey was bored. He gave his handsome head a shake, flipping his thick beard back and forth with a muted swish that sent his goaty perfume drifting across the driveway. Petulantly, he lifted one of his cumbersome, cloven feet, laying it on the wire of the fence, working the wire back and forth a little, testing its mettle. The wire swayed and creaked against its staples. His weight was prodigious. He probably could have pushed right through the fence, but he'd been penned up for so long, that this option never occurred to him.

He blinked. Feeling an itch beginning to develop on his right flank, he let go of the fence, took a step, and leaned ponderously into the wooden gate, scratching himself against the rough boards for the hundredth time. This time something new happened. With a sharp report the throw bolt on the outside of the gate sprang loose, and the gate flew open like a frightened bird. Screws and staples went flying. Joey almost fell through the gate, but caught himself like a true mountaineer, then calmly turned and observed the opening.

A heretofore unreachable tuft of bright green grass beckoned to him from no-goat's-land. He leaned forward with questing lips, and for the first time found no barrier, so took a hesitating step, and was rewarded with a crunchy chaw. He chewed quickly and swallowed. Then, having broken the spell of the fence, and feeling the sharp desire for more exotic fare, he ambled on through the gate. The other goats, seeing the flash of his upright tail, followed anxiously in his wake, baaing with consternation. They were afraid to abandon the familiarity of their yard but were unwilling to be separated from Joey.

Meanwhile, an idea was welling up in the big goat's slow brain. He'd been slavering for a nibble of that little cedar of Lebanon tree all summer. Now his nose flared at the resinous smell and, having made up his mind, he picked up speed, trotting over the stony fairway, leading the entire herd down the driveway at a very fast trot.

Tree in trouble. I can still see them, heads down, yellow, slotted eyes focused greedily ahead, pausing not for a moment to nip daisy or tomato, bound straight for the juicy bark of that unusual tree. Before any of us could reach the scene of the crime, the goats clustered around the poor tree like hounds on a coon, stripping off long strips of slippy bark, and then putting back their heads to chew, glorying in the taste, masticating in bliss. Before we could drive them off, they denuded the poor tree from base to breast, leaving only a narrow strip uneaten. The sun glistened on the wounded trunk.

Leaving the children to guard the tree from further damage, I raced to the goat shed, mounted the steps, vaulted into the main room, and jiggled the grain barrel. Hearing this, and thinking unaccountably that they now deserved to eat some grain, all the goats stampeded back up the driveway, through the open gate and into their enclosure. By the way, this is the main advice that natural gardening techniques gives us about goats—when the routine falls apart, never, ever let them know what you truly desire, for they will do the exact opposite!

I ran around the shed and closed in my naughty herd, then propped a board against the gate, stemming the urge to beat them with the board. What use would it serve? The damage was already done! I walked back, kicking the gravel of the driveway with each step, to where my little clan was huddled around the wounded tree. Together we examined it closely. To our surprise, there was hope. The strip of bark that had not been chewed was still in one piece, a narrow lifeline between roots and branches. We conjectured that if it could be preserved from drying out, well, the tree might heal itself.

"Use comfrey salve!" chimed one of the kids. "That's silly," I almost replied, but then thought better of it. Actually, if we smeared comfrey salve at the sides of the strip of healthy bark, it might serve to keep the bark moist and make it less likely to peel back and crack. Perhaps the comfrey would engender new growth—it certainly worked on humans.

"That," I said, "is a brilliant idea!" Nadja went into the apothecary and pulled from the shelf my mightiest jar of salve. The children and I spread the waxy green substance all over the naked wound, smearing liberally at the edges. Someone ran in and got an old cotton sheet from the house, and we ripped it into long bandages. Then, we tightly wrapped the wounded trunk, being careful to exert plenty of pressure on the bark bridge, willing it to adhere to the wood. Around bedtime that night, I was to discover that the sheet had come from my bed . . .

Over the ensuing days, we anxiously watched the aerial parts of our precious cedar to see if they would droop, and it was a vast relief that the tree never showed a single sign of stress. We resisted the temptation to peek inside the bandages to see how the wound was faring. After a few weeks, I palpitated the area, and detected the swelling of new bark at the edges. "Hey," I shouted, "it's healing!"

The kids were involved in a project, but they looked up, nodded, and smiled. Later, I discovered the reason for their lack of interest. They'd been in the middle of inventing a "cable car," which promised an activity that would be sufficiently dangerous to trump any other events. They were planning to swing from a board that was attached to a rope that was tied to a pulley that was stretched to a cable that ran from the bank of the creek down to a tree limb in the creek bottoms. This is the kind of project that is hatched by young people who are encouraged from an early age to be creative and fearless!

Sometime the following spring, the weatherworn bandages on the cedar tree spontaneously ruptured and fell away of their own accord. The tree showed off its new bark, which, to our amazement, had completely grown back over the bare wood. Now, many years later, the tree is as big around as a barrel and spreads wide its hefty branches. The bark of the trunk is, unaccountably, perfect and unblemished. I attribute this to the healing power of comfrey.

Growing trees from seed. I like to grow trees from seed. I know it takes a long time for them to mature, but this is really no excuse for not planting them. They're not just for us, you know. They're for the worm, and robin, and crow. We humans derive so much from trees, including things made of wood like toilet paper, coffee cups, baseball bats, bedknobs, and bookshelves. Trees also give us nourishment with their fruits and nuts. They are a significant source of medicines. Trees also give shade from the sun, help hold water in the earth, and make oxygen for us to breathe. We owe trees a lot. It is good karma to give something back to the trees by planting them. And, they are really cute when they germinate!

Growing ginkgo trees from seed. If you're lucky, you can find some ginkgo fruits under an already established female tree. Ginkgos have been planted in many places: in yards in the city, along roadways, in graveyards, and on the lawns of college campuses. They are a stately and handsome tree. Each ginkgo fruit contains one large seed. Bring the fruits home. Don't put the bare-naked fruits right in your pocket, because they will squish, and they don't smell very nice—carry them in a plastic bag or some other impermeable container. When you get home, smash the fruits by hand under a cold-water faucet to wash away the sticky flesh. What you have left is the seed itself: edible, heavy, vibrant, cream-colored, smooth, and—fragrant.

Ginkgo seed must be given about 30 days of cold-conditioning before it will sprout. Put the seed in some moist sand in a plastic bag and keep it in the fridge for a month. Then, remove the seed from the plastic bag and plant it in a gallon pot located on a sunny windowsill or better yet, in the greenhouse. The seedling will emerge in another 30 days. If you don't have a sunny spot, then you don't have to put the seed in the refrigerator. Just plant it in a gallon pot and leave the pot outside in a protected location. The winter will provide the cold-conditioning, and the seed will germinate with the warming of the soil in the spring.

Why choose ginkgo? One reason might be because the tree grows so slowly that planting it is of necessity a selfless act. Any planting of the tree is really a gift to a later generation. The Chinese call it "the grandmother granddaughter tree," implying that the grandmother plants the tree for the enjoyment of the grandchild.

Another reason to choose ginkgo is because you are likely to see good results, and I want you to be happy and successful in your attempts to grow trees from seed. Ginkgo seeds are large and, if the right process is followed, they are relatively easy to germinate and grow. Plant 3 per pot, because the normal germination rate is only about 40%. This will be very likely to give you at least 1 good seedling per pot. Hopefully, your success with ginkgo will prime your pump, so to speak, and if so, it will be your good fortune to continue to sow the seeds of trees. Mix them some fast-draining soil (see Chapter 18 — Potting Soils). Grow tree seedlings out in successively larger pots for 1 or 2 years, and then when they are robust enough to survive, find a good place to plant them on the landscape. Beautiful people, the earth needs us to plant lots of trees. Let's get to work!

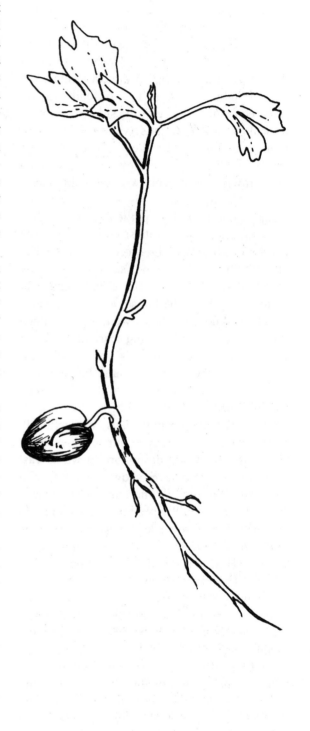

CHAPTER 11 — HUMANS

Define human access. A local grower traded me a number of semidwarf fruit trees for doing some fieldwork in his echinacea patch. It took me a few days to get the trees planted, during which time I had a good excuse for not fulfilling my trade, but eventually payback time did arrive. So one bright morning, we approached his echinacea field with stirrup hoes in hand, intent on doing a good bout of weeding. The echinacea was planted down in the creek bottoms, next to a riparian zone of maples, firs, ferns, and blackberries.

I was walking casually down the field, when he mentioned that actually I was walking *on* another crop. My mortification must have been great, because I still remember that the crop was goat's rue (*Galega officinalis*), which at the time I couldn't really differentiate from the weeds. "Oh, so sorry!" I exclaimed, jumping off to the side. The grower shrugged it off, saying, "It's all right, they like it."

Although goat's rue is pretty tough, I don't think it really liked being stepped on, but this experience brought me a couple of lessons I'll never forget: 1) Set things up so people know where to walk and where not to walk. 2) If they do walk on the plants, be kind, not grumpy. OK, OK, so I still have a ways to go on the "grumpy" part, but I have some really good ideas about how to let people know where to walk. In reality, I take pains to improve the paths, so my grumpiness quotient need not be tested.

Grasses and mowing grasses. There are many ways to define human access, and one of the best is by mowing the pathways. Most people know that in the garden, it's allowed to walk on the grass. This is a sort of universal agreement that need not be explained. Mowed grass perimeters and pathways give a very kempt appearance to the entire garden. I'm not sure if this preference for mowing derives from my middle class suburban upbringing, or if it can be attributed to a more universal design element—clearer demarcations in the landscape.

Grass tends to spring up in the open areas between the cultivated portions of the land. Grass is nature's own blanket—she covers herself with it whenever the land is laid bare. If grass does not automatically grow in the pathways between your crops, you can always seed it in. If there is a concern that grasses will get out of hand and get in around the perennials, then plant annual ryegrass. Otherwise, orchard grass (or whatever grass volunteers for you) will be just fine. If the land is very sloped, uneven or stony, or if the grass is overgrown, then a hand-held weed whip or a pushable weed trimmer will do a better job than the bladed lawnmower.

The weed trimmer is shaped just like a standard lawnmower, but is not phased by rocks, tall grass, or overgrown weeds. As opposed to the hand-held weed whip, the weed trimmer is held up by its own wheels, and this machine can be run for a really long time on a very small tank of gas. In fact, despite the ergonomic advantage of this weed trimmer, the farmer is likely to run out of gas before the machine does.

Pathways. Make the path wide, as creeping plants and flowers will soon narrow it. The minimum working width for an outdoor path is 4 feet. Better to plan for 6 feet wide—wider at entryways. People will tarry longer on wider paths, and in the forest, wide paths let in more sun. A good path will meander so as to maximize surface area in contact with plants.

Paths can be designed to lead to the best niches, even if it doesn't otherwise make sense to go that way. Here's where you show off the shiitake mushroom log, or the gnome hole in that old oak, or the Jack-in-the-pulpit patch. A well-worn path will attract more soles.

People bumpers. Another excellent feature for defining human access (letting people know where they may walk and where they jolly-well-better-not walk) is the "people bumper." This is a low curb, made of wood or stone, dividing off the pathway from the garden beds. In the full sun, rocks, blocks, bricks, or even cement can be utilized to good advantage. In the forest or shade garden, it makes sense to employ cooler, softer borders made of logs or planks. Put down a strip of weed barrier underneath the edges of garden beds (regardless of whether they are made of rock, or wood, or what have you), and then mulch over the top and up against the people bumper with bark or sawdust. This will cover up the ugly weed barrier, while it reduces the labor required to keep the edges clear of grasses and other weeds.

Entryways and gates. "Well begun is half done." Gates are appropriately placed at the entryway to the land, the home zone, the garden, and especially as a way into or out of any enclosures for farm animals. Make these gateways easily functional, roomy, and inviting. Large boulders set to the side of the gate create a feeling of solidity and, unlike the small borders of decorative rock that are sometimes employed, large stones won't get lost in the grass and will be less likely to end up under the blade of the lawnmower. Such boulders are good for defining margins to the side, creating the open arms of a wide pathway leading up to a gateway vaulted over with a trellis. Next to the boulders, and protected by them, plants can be set in, and trained up the sides of the gate onto the trellis. Climbing roses, true gourds (*Lagenaria siceraria*), trumpet vine creepers, hops, wisteria, and Chinese wild yams make excellent choices for trellising around gates.

The gate itself deserves special attention, as rustic designs truly augment the flowers. Gates are best made to swing open easily, yet secure tightly. Natural materials, such as weathered boards and wrought iron hinges, are a nice touch. Keep the gates in top repair. The condition of the gate often reflects the condition of the land as a whole. Create "farm-schwei" by keeping the entryway clear of things like that twisted spaghetti of garden hose, the wheelbarrow with the flat tire, the pile of rotting debris that nobody seems to be able to get around to throwing out on the compost pile, and the empty plastic pot, split up the side and left kicking around when that pot-bound horseradish that Uncle Charlie

gifted you last year final. bondage and planted in patch. Grass in front of ↙ mowed short and raked free Excellent plants for decking o gateways include stately rose ↙ants, Krishna tulsi (which is traditional.y planted at entryways to bring good fortune), or bright flowers, such as cowslip, Johnny-jump-ups, or nasturtiums.

Upkeep is not only about deadheading the daisies, oiling the hinges, and picking up the rake so nobody gets beaned—it's also about maintaining the etheric energy of the gateway. When building, gardening around, or walking through the gate, it helps to think positive thoughts about those who will come through, and how much love and peace they will experience when entering the garden.

A doorway can be a beginning or an end or a way through into another state of consciousness. It would be nice to make our garden doorways like this—an invitation to suspend, for a spell, the worries of human culture and connect more directly with the native state. "Enter here and think no more."

CHAPTER 12 — THE FOREST COMMUNITY

Frolicking in the woods. On a hot day here on the farm, we are likely to take refuge in the woods down by the creek. Summer breezes are cooled as they pass through the tree leaves, over the moist woodland soil, and across the cold water. The creek originates in snow melt, water born high in mountain meadows, seeping, trickling down, finding its way, picking up speed, eventually chattering as it bounds over the rounded rocks of its stony bed. If we're really hot, we may brave a dip in a bright green pool. Even on the hottest days, this brings the body temperature down just as quickly as it brings up our gasping shouts of joy!

After a bit of rest in the shade, we find things to do down in the woods: picking up fallen limbs, thinning the jewelweed patch, trellising the wild yams, firming down the soil around the goldenseal where some burrowing animal has heaved it up, gently squeezing the bloodroot seedpods to gauge their ripeness, or pulling up the populous, shrubby snowberries to make another bed for a projected fall planting of blue cohosh.

The herbs of the eastern hardwood forest biome are at the heart of western herbalism. Black cohosh, bloodroot, goldenseal, and ginseng are such essential herbal medicines that it is really worth it to grow them whenever circumstances allow. Luckily, these plants are much more highly adaptable to varied ecologies than you might think. Given the right soil and protection from the sun, they can be planted directly in the shade garden or grown in pots in the shadehouse.

The best way to grow them, regardless of whether you live to the east of the Rockies or to the west, is under a natural canopy of hardwood trees. Cultivating plants in the forest is, in many ways, easier than cultivating plants out in the full sun. In the forest, one finds a rich, moist soil that needs no tillage or fertilization. Perhaps the best news of all is that in the half-light of the woodlands, few weeds will grow.

When gardening in the forest, disturb the soil as little as possible and make use of resources that are already present. The trees really do the majority of the work for us: building the soil, providing free shade during the hotter parts of the year, disallowing the grasses, and gently and completely mulching the herbs with their leaves in the fall.

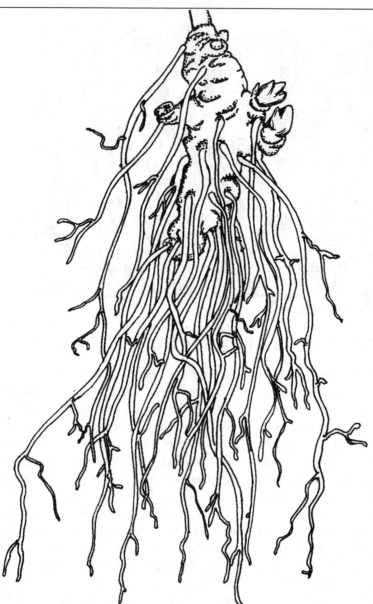

The root-rhizome structure. Black cohosh, bloodroot, blue cohosh, goldenseal, trillium, mayapple, Solomon's seal, stoneroot, and wild yam are all good examples of forest plants, and they all have one thing in common— their stems rise up from a root-rhizome structure. See the illustration of goldenseal, above, for a classic example of a root-rhizome structure. The true roots of these plants are hair-like, emanating from the bottom of the rhizome, delving deeply into the soil, sequestering water and nutrients. The roots of these forest plants are not taproots, which would be more typical to prairie plants. The roots of forest plants are more properly termed *feeder roots*. The rhizome itself is a highly evolved underground storage chamber that is also the seat of life for the plant. Usually oriented horizontally, the rhizome lies buried just beneath the soil surface. For the purpose of understanding how to propagate the forest plants, it is good to know the difference between a hair-like mass of feeder roots and a stocky rhizome. The root-rhizome structure is also known simply as "the root."

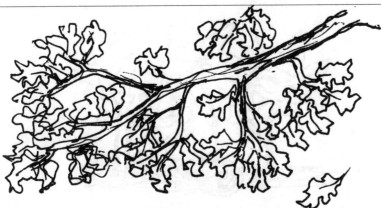

Forest soil is formed as layers of leaves compost down into rich, dark soil, which is full of moisture, nutrients, humus, and living organisms. In the forest, the primary organisms breaking down raw carbon into humus are fungal mycelia. These are the body of the mushroom—a network of white, spongy material that can be readily observed when you examine the layers of leaf mould and twig. Below this lies the mixture of mineral soil and humus that makes up the proverbial sandy loam, the predominant soil type found in healthy hardwood forests. If you dig deeper, you may discover layers of clay or water-deposited sand and gravel, because where there are trees, the water has probably never been very far away.

Mycorrhizae. Forest loam supports the growth of mycorrhizal fungi that live in, on, and around the roots of many herbs. The mycorrhizae break down carbon and minerals into soluble forms that are easily assimilated by the host plant. Mycorrhizae interface between the plant and its environment, improving the ability of the roots to uptake nutrients and water, and also extending the reach of the plant's roots. Mycorrhizae help protect plants from temperature extremes, drought, and disease. In return, the plant feeds starch and simple sugars to the fungi, which are organisms that know how to do a lot with a little. Growing plants in real dirt in a forest or in an organic garden really supports this symbiosis. Is it then any surprise that a plant grown in this way provides a whole and balanced medicine?

Cultivating plants within the woodlands may be as simple an act as pushing a fresh goldenseal seed into a bit of bare soil, or it may involve planting live roots or root cuttings. In natural gardening, you take advantage of whatever likely opportunities present themselves. The typical microsite is a spongy patch of ground (perhaps covered with a thick layer of leaf mulch, or the site of a clump of plants like violets or cleavers that you will have to remove) near a stump or a rock. Stumps and rocks are nice because they serve to mark the spot and may help keep animals from stepping on the new plant. They are indicators for dappled shade, cannot compete with the plant for nutrients, and provide the plant with air space and shelter from the wind. Fallen logs are good companions for the same reasons, and also because they provide habitat for fungi and beneficial insects. Fallen logs are also a source of mulch and, in good time, new soil.

Finding your site. Within the mixed hardwood forest, rich soil will form wherever the hardwoods are dropping their leaves. Fallen leaves and woody detritus decompose into humus. Soil will tend to accrue in low spots and at the base of the treed slope. I call this "soil puddling." Bringing a spade with you into the woods can really help you find these areas of deeper soil, and these are good places to locate patches of medicinal herbs. Push the spade in as you go along, to determine where the soil is deep, soft, and free of woody roots and rocks.

Planting roots. Without much site preparation, you can usually find room to plant a ginseng root here and a goldenseal cutting there. You can move aside some mulch up next to a stump and push your spade into the loam, pull back the soil, dangle the roots down in the hole behind the shovel, swiftly remove the shovel, and tamp in the soil around the root, making short work of it, introducing a valuable new plant to a receptive habitat. Once you cover the spot again with mulch, the earth hardly knows it's been opened, but it is now charged with a special, new plant. This is a good thing to do. After all, people have been going through the woods and *removing* a ginseng here, a goldenseal there, for many generations, so in replanting you are bringing back the original balance. In order to grow a substantial amount of medicine in the woods (say a 20-foot bed, which would eventually produce enough root to make a gallon or so of gold-enseal tincture), then it will probably be necessary to prepare a bed, where the plants can be properly cared for *en masse*.

Although forest plants are shade lovers, they nonetheless are photosynthetic. A dappled shade situation (about 50 to 80% shade), with sunlight streaming through from time to time, is ideal, producin high yields of roots, fruits, and seeds. Deep forest plants like bloodroot and blue cohosh need more shade, and plants of the forest edge (like black cohosh and wild yam) do better with more light.

You will probably have to brush out your site and remove lower branches from some of the trees. Clear the paths and cut away any dead branches and potential head-bangers. You might even have to selectively harvest some trees in order to bring more light into the growing areas. Make sure to preserve the larger, well-formed trees and remove the weak, diseased, or poorly formed trees. Pile all woody debris so that it can eventually melt down and become good soil. In the meantime, your pile of sticks will serve as habitat for songbirds and frogs.

Any cleared space in the forest tends to become a pathway for humans and animals that pass through or live there, so it is very important to define paths *alongside* of your beds, otherwise people and animals will be walking *on* your beds. Along the same lines, it makes sense to clear your growing areas, but leave other areas untouched. Native bushes and snarls of small trees and understory plants serve as habitat and an alternate source of food for birds and wild animals. The turkeys can eat wild raspberries—not goldenseal berries!

After the brush has been removed from the planting site, remove any creeping green plants. (Sorry, cleavers, but there's lots of you out there!) Now rake the area clear of leaf mulch and heap the mulch to the side of the bed. You will need it later.

The new bed snakes off between the tree trunks in the half-light, the dark earth open and beckoning. Perhaps a few earthworms crawl out to investigate. The next step is to dig shallow furrows across the bed. An axe and a garden fork may be needed, along with the spade. Dig the furrows 1 foot apart for small plants (e.g. goldenseal and bloodroot) and

2 feet apart for larger plants (e.g. black and blue cohosh). Digging the furrow gives you an opportunity to remove rocks and some of the many tree roots that would otherwise impede the growth of your plantings.

Alternate rows and beds. In nature, the plants grow in a mixed and complimentary ecosystem, which is resilient in the face of stressors, such as browsers, slugs, and insect pests. Although cultivating more extensive patches of herbs provides the opportunity to grow many plants in a small space, it is important to avoid the pitfall of the monocrop. Be sure to alternate rows of different plants in the beds or alternate the beds themselves, first ginseng, then goldenseal, then blue cohosh, etc. The mixed plantings will sequester mycorrhizae and attract pollinators. Mixed plantings result in improved fruit set, overall drought tolerance, and resistance to diseases and insect pests.

It is best to allow the newly planted beds to overwinter without any further disturbance. Winter rains, snow cover, and low temperatures are not only well-tolerated, but *needed* by most forest-dependent medicinal herbs. Without this period of cold dormancy, the plants will not survive and thrive. If the winter is very dry, without much rain or snow, then it will be necessary to give supplemental water, as the roots must not dry out in the winter. The plants are somewhat more resilient in the face of summer drought, because by summer the extended root system and mycorrhizal associations are already intact.

Naturalizing. Once the forest plants emerge in the spring, they will pretty much take care of themselves. There is little to do except enjoy them, but there are a few tasks that might arise. It's a good idea to stick some branches in around the wild yams to give them something to climb on. You will certainly want to remove any slugs from the area. If the summer is very dry, you may need to water the beds. This is particularly important in the west, where we have dry summers and dry air. Forest plants do not like dry air—they like humidity.

It usually takes 2 years for forest plants started from roots or root cuttings to become accustomed to their new home and really dig in. You will know they are happy when they mature their fruit and start to spread of their own accord. This is known as naturalizing.

Cycles and seasons. During the spring and summer, the forest plant stores energy reserves in the rhizome, mainly in the form of starch. This energy is then utilized by the plant when needed, especially during dormancy. During the growing period, the rhizome is also charged with secondary compounds. Unique to each plant, these are the active constituents that are mainly responsible for the plant's medicinal activity. For example, the golden-hued isoquinoline alkaloids found in goldenseal are largely responsible for the antibacterial activity of the plant. These alkaloids are present at highest concentrations in the rhizome and the root hairs. In another example, the bitter digestive principles inherent in calamus (*Acorus calamus*) are found in much higher concentrations in the rhizome than in the roots. Therefore, good quality calamus herb consists of the rhizome freed from its rootlets. In olden times, herbalists were known as "root doctors" for good reason—they understood that the strongest medicine of many plants resides below ground!

In nature, the development of the forest plant is cyclic. In the spring, the buds elongate and become stems and leaves, eventually producing flowers, fruits, and seeds. In the fall, the aerial parts of the plant die back down to the rhizome. At the same time, as the soil cools, the roots undergo rapid development, elongating and re-establishing the network of feeder roots below the plant. This process of sending out feeder roots may occur during dormancy any time the soil temperature and moisture are conducive.

So you see, the energy flow within the plant is aerial from spring through summer, and subterranean from fall through the winter. Therefore, the best time for transplant is *in the fall*. Fall-planted rhizomes root in, gain a sense of place through the winter and ready themselves for normal, vigorous development come spring.

The best time for harvest is also seasonally determined. Roots are best harvested during the dormancy of fall to early spring, and aerial parts are best harvested during the spring and early summer. Some exceptions (such as the time-honored act of harvesting bloodroot rhizomes in May) exist, but for the most part the seasonal rules do apply.

Starting plants from root cuttings is the best way to quickly establish adult flowering individuals in the forest. These individuals will make seed, and the resulting plants will produce mature roots for the purpose of medicine making. Although the plants themselves do a pretty good job of disseminating their seed, it sure doesn't hurt to give them a helping hand.

I'll never forget my first lesson in this. I was walking in the Kentucky woods with my friend, Orville, and he reached down to pluck a swollen bloodroot pod. Squeezing the ripe seeds out into his hand, he showed them to me, resting red-brown against his work-worn palm. Then, with a sweeping motion of his arm, he scattered them into the forest. I could hear them hitting the leaves and falling back down to the earth. "Does that really work?" I asked. He looked at me, smiled, and said, "Yep."

PART 2

PRACTICES OF NATURAL GARDENING TECHNIQUES

CHAPTER 13 — BACKGROUND

Early peoples must have observed that seeds deposited in or on the ground occasionally undergo a metamorphosis and become plants. With hunger at stake, it wouldn't have taken long for our predecessors to realize that plants growing around the human settlement, where there was ready availability of nitrogen, sunlight, and water, often grew larger, tasted better, were easier to harvest, and even perhaps easier to digest than their wild counterparts.

The first growers of plants were probably Neolithic hunters and gatherers who (at first fortuitously and later intentionally) spread seeds onto the village refuse pile (the tribal version of our modern day compost pile) and took advantage of the resulting plants when they grew big enough to eat. There is a direct relationship between the high fertility that occurred around early human settlements and the first domestication of wild plants.

The Koster Site. This version of the early roots of gardening is shaped by my experiences as an archaeologist. Digging away at the prehistoric Koster Site in Southern Illinois, I learned that layers of soil deposited during times of human settlement were dark in color,

being rich in organic compounds and charcoal. The stone tools and bones found in these dark-colored strata evidenced a series of sporadic human occupations dating all the way back to 7,500 B.C. At this time, people roamed the Midwestern river valleys and set up camp wherever the foraging, fishing, and hunting was good. Pottery had not yet been invented.

As we delved down through the ages at the Koster site, it also became evident that soils deposited at times when humans were absent tended to be sterile and lighter colored, and of course contained no artifacts at all. The juxtaposition of dark and fertile "occupied" strata over buff-colored, "sterile" strata became obvious when one looked at the walls of the excavation, which showed a layered effect, dark and light like a chocolate and vanilla layer cake. In contemplating this stratigraphy, it began to dawn on me that tribal humans had a profound influence on the land where they lived. The organic materials that they brought into the settlement ended up fertilizing the land to such an extent that the difference was still visible thousands of years later.

Humans profoundly effect the land. All that organic debris, I posited, must have made their surroundings very much like a garden. This situation would have strongly encouraged early peoples to experiment with domestication of plants and, once they learned to grow plants at will, this must have encouraged them to settle down in one place. I contemplated the gentle symbiosis that takes place between people and fertile soil, where gardeners fertilize the soil with discarded debris from the plants they are growing, and the soil, so nurtured, feeds the people with nutritious foods. I then realized that this symbiosis represents the natural state of humans living in balance with the earth, a lifestyle that worked for early peoples and *is still relevant* for us in modern times. I wanted to test my hypothesis about the fertility of this ancient soil by using some of it to grow a crop.

Growing watermelons story. Everything clicked one afternoon in Kampsville, the tiny riverside town where we archaeologists (known to the locals as "arkies") had our base of operations. I was shopping at the tiny Kampsville country store when I spied a brightly colored packet of watermelon seeds hanging on a wire rack. To the surprise of the proprietor, who must have wondered why an arkie needed garden seeds, I bought them outright and slipped them into my back pocket.

The next day, back at the Koster Site, I filled a wheelbarrow full of black dirt (don't worry, it had already been sifted through to remove the artifacts) that had come from one of the occupied strata. I ran the wheelbarrow back around to the surface (Theodore Koster's old cornfield) and dumped it in a tidy hill just above the excavation. Then I firmed the hill, poked a few holes in the dark soil, opened my packet of seeds, dropped the seeds in the holes, and patted them down lovingly, willing them to sprout.

A few days later, the seedlings emerged into the hot and humid southern Illinois sunlight. I tended my little charges daily, bringing dipperfuls of clear cold water from a brick-lined artesian fountain that welled up on the hillside near the farmhouse. As the plants entered their vegetative stage, they sent their long runners merrily cascading down the walls of the deep excavation, tendriling from the present, as it were, back through history. This delighted me, but was somewhat of a concern to the scientist in charge, who nonetheless allowed my plant to drape down over the stratigraphy. Finally, in a testament to the fertility of those ancient soils, the watermelon made bright yellow flowers that soon transformed into promising, round fruits, right on top of the early archaic period at 6,000 B.C.!

I'm sad to report that I never tasted any ripe melons from that eager vine, as the summer's work ended with a torrential rainstorm that threatened to fill the entire excavation like a giant, community swimming pool. However, I had proven my point—the watermelons grew in that anciently fertilized soil as if growing in the finest of compost.

Pigweed porridge hot. The identification of pollen and charred seeds found in fire pits within the dark strata at the Koster site revealed that lamb's quarters (*Chenopodium alba*) and pigweed (*Amaranthus* sp.) were common plants in that place in ancient times. Furthermore, we discovered metates (grinding stones) dating back to 6,400 B.C., which was good evidence that people were grinding the seeds into flour. The presence of charred seeds found throughout the various occupied strata implied cooking. These early peoples were probably starting their day by eating porridge or hearty fire-baked bread made of pounded seeds! Most gardeners are familiar with lamb's quarters and pigweed as edible weeds of cultivated ground. It is fascinating to think that these plants that still volunteer so readily in our summer gardens have been doing so for at least 10,000 years.

The Neolithic time period is characterized as a revolutionary phase of human development, when human populations increased and the availability of wild resources decreased. Around this time, early experimentation with domesticating wild plants swiftly developed into the coordinated cultivation of food crops. Agriculture became the best method for feeding ever increasing populations of sedentary peoples.

The plant-human relationship. A kind of co-evolution took place, with people relying on plants for food, shelter, clothing, and medicine, and plants relying on people for their very existence. There was mutual dependency. The cultivated plants could no longer make it in the wilds, because they needed humans to cultivate the land and to store and disseminate their seeds. On the human side, the free-ranging lifestyle of the hunter and gatherer eating wild meat gave way to the more peaceful lifestyle of gardener and winnower eating bread.

These days, the situation with medicinal herbs is actually quite similar to what occurred with food plants during the Neolithic. To a large extent, up until very recently, we have been hunters and gatherers of our herbal medicines. However, human population is increasing and wild medicinal herbs are diminishing. So in order to maintain a ready supply of medicinal herbs, we again turn to domesticating wild plants in order to provide needed herbal medicines. For instance, a great deal of echinacea tincture is consumed in the US. Historically, this tincture was made from the roots of *Echinacea angustifolia* harvested from the wild. However, wild populations cannot sustain the high level of consumer demand for this remedy, and so now, for the most part, the echinacea tincture that is consumed in the US is made from the roots of domestically cultivated *Echinacea purpurea*.

On the domestication of plants. Plants can be usefully characterized according to their degree of domestication. Those that have been extensively cultivated and selected are known as *cultigens*. These plants have been transformed from their original wild form by horticulturalists (scientists, gardeners, or farmers) through years of selective breeding. The wild progenitor, if not extinct, is at least very different from the garden plant as we know it. The classic example of this is corn (*Zea mays*), which was selected over many generations from its wild ancestor, *teosinte* (*Zea mexicana*). *Teosinte* hardly resembles an ear of cultivated corn, as it bears only a single row of kernels in its tiny cob, but it is the wild progenitor of a plant that feeds the world.

Herbal cultigens. A good example of an herbal cultigen would be calendula (*Calendula officinalis*), which was probably originally derived from wild calendula (*Calendula arvensis*), a plant of the Mediterranean basin that produces a lush green bush studded with many small yellow flowers. How did this transformation from wild plant to garden medicinal occur? Selection can be almost unintentional, in that gardeners tend to save seed from the plants with the largest flowers. After a few growing seasons of doing this, they find that *all* their plants have larger flowers. In the case of calendula, where the main medicinal activity of the plant actually resides in the flowers, selection of this sort probably serves to augment the medicine, resulting in increased production of anti-inflammatory flavonoids and antiseptic resins.

When domesticating plants, the grower automatically selects for ease of germination. This is because the seeds that germinate most readily produce the plants that we save. These plants eventually produce the next generation of seed-producing plants. The process of domestication begins with the plant as it is found in nature and is fulfilled when the plant is sufficiently tamed to grow easily in the domestic garden. A few good examples of cultigens used in herbalism are the cultivated forms of: angelica, asparagus, basil, beans, bitter melon, borage, chamomile, chicory, marshmallow, garden sage, summer savory, parsley, poppies, and valerian.

The challenge of domesticating wild plants. Wild plants, like children who have spent a whole summer running barefoot in the fields and brooks and then are required to put on leather shoes and go to school, may be resistant to domestication. This is perhaps nowhere more evident than in a comparison of germination times of domesticated *versus* nondomesticated species of closely related plants. For instance, in the above-mentioned wild calendula, germination is very slow and incomplete, often requiring cold-conditioning for the seed to germinate, while the standard domesticated yellow and orange calendula is a reliable germinator that may be planted throughout the growing season with predictably good results. Another example would be the germination of domesticated *versus* nondomesticated forms of basil. Germination of standard basil (e.g. *Ocimum basilicum* "lettuce leaf") is usually 6 days in standard greenhouse culture, while germination of a wild form of basil (*Ocimum canum* "African basil") demonstrates incomplete and ongoing germination beginning as long as 2 to 4 weeks after planting. So, cultivating food crops and *domesticated* medicinals can be likened to raising a dog, while cultivating *wild* medicinal herbs is a bit more like raising a wolf!

The seeds of some wild herbs must be kept moist in order to maintain viability, or they may require long germination periods, the passage of seasons, or the confluence of a particular set of conditions of light, temperature and moisture before germination is possible. The season when various wild plants naturally drop their seed will vary, and an understanding of this natural cycle will help the gardener decide when best to plant the same seeds in the garden.

Many of the long-germinating wild seeds do best when planted in the fall—not the spring. Wild herbs may also be pretty particular about where they will grow, often requiring a specific econiche to feel completely at home, and failing if they are planted in the wrong place. Conditions inimical to the growth of standard garden varieties, such as burning hot sand or the full shade of a hardwood canopy, may well be exactly what certain wild herbs require. A few examples of plants that remain on the wild side even under domestication would be arnica, black cohosh, chickweed, cleavers, echinacea, goldenseal, devil's club, jewelweed, licorice, ma-huang, mandrake, mullein, passionflower, skullcap, white sage, and wild yam.

The degree to which the plant is domesticated is usually a good indication of how easy it will be to grow it. Really, the degree of domestication is an ever-evolving continuum. Some wild plants are well-behaved in the domestic garden (like self-heal growing in compost) and some plants remain unruly despite their familiarity to us (like dandelion growing inside the cracks of the sidewalk).

Cultivars, hybrids, select strains, and GMO's. There is another very prolific group of plants known as the "named cultivars," which often carry rather flippant names (e.g. "*Lavandula angustifolia* var. twickel purple purple"). The named cultivars are varieties selected for particular traits (usually disease resistance or flower color) and consequently they differ from the wild form. Such plants are often asexually propagated clones that will not breed true from seed.

Another problem with named cultivars is that when the breeder brings one trait (say, flower color) in the front door, they unwittingly let another trait (say, fragrance) out the back door. Plants can only hold so much, and when one trait is enhanced and the plant gains a varietal name, it may well lose some of its medicinal potency as an unwitting consequence. For example, it is pretty well accepted that the open-pollinated wild form of lavender known as true English lavender (*Lavandula angustifolia vera*) gives the highest grade of essential oils. Hybrid lavenders and named varieties may be pretty, but they contain a lower quality of essential oil, which of course is indicative of the medicinal value of the plant.

I am particularly leery of hybridization, tissue culture, and genetic modification of medicinal plants. I think these processes alter the concentration and/or kind of medicinal compounds, rendering the plant less predictable and less dependable for medicinal use. If we rely on traditional wisdom to tell us how to use the herbs, then where will this leave us if we change the traditional makeup of the plant? In conclusion, steer clear of named cultivars, hybrids, and GMO's, opting instead for heirloom varieties or the open-pollinated wild form of the plant.

It is true that some progress has been made in selecting certain strains of medicinal plants for higher levels of secondary compounds (otherwise popularly known as active constituents). This has been done with, for instance, German chamomile, garden sage, and valerian, but I'm not sure if this kind of tinkering really produces a better medicinal plant. We don't fully understand what it is in plants that makes them work as medicines. Plants contain complex admixtures of active constituents, and selecting for high levels of one may result in the diminution of another, with a resulting loss of balance in the medicine.

Compounds in plants. Food crops are loaded with tasty *primary* compounds, such as starch, sugar, and protein. Garden vegetables and cultivated grains provide life-giving nutrients, even more so when the plants are properly cultivated, weeded, watered, and fertilized. Over time, farmers have endeavored to select our food crops for improved texture, taste, yield, and storability. They have chosen strains of plants for disease resistance, frost hardiness, quick maturity, high yield, and consistent edibility. Farmers have also chosen seeds that are tolerant of dry storage and concentrated on developing varieties that can be planted in the spring to mature within a single growing season These are all attributes that make plants more dependable as food.

Breeding plants for food use may involve selecting for a lower concentration of nonfood elements, the variously aromatic, acrid, bitter, or even toxic *secondary* compounds, such as: alkaloids, terpenoids, saponins, and glycosides. These compounds exist in the plant tissues at a relatively low concentration compared to the primary compounds, and they have little food value for humans, but they are the source of most of our plant medicines. Medicinal herbs freely fix these secondary compounds in their tissues or exude them into the outer environment as a means of attracting pollinators, repelling browsers, defending themselves, or communicating with other plants, insects, and vertebrates—including humans.

Whether or not certain secondary compounds are produced by the plant intentionally in order to assist *Homo sapiens* is a topic still under debate. However, it is an undeniable fact, that the complex admixtures of secondary compounds found in plants have a profound and potentially therapeutic influence on the human organism.

The medicinal herb gardener wants to produce an herb that is rich in medicinal compounds comparable to those found in the herb as it exists in the wild. Already accustomed to cooperating with nature while setting up the conditions to successfully germinate the seeds, the gardener further strives to provide a growth environment not too far removed from the natural state, creating habitat similar to what the plants would encounter in the wild.

Medicinal compounds may also be produced not by the plant itself, but by other organisms that live on, in, or in very close association with the plant. Medicinal plant research continues to reveal plant-bacteria associations that produce medicinally significant active compounds. For instance, research is showing that a bacterial endophyte is responsible at least in part for the immune enhancing effects of echinacea. The compounds, known as lipoproteins and lipopolysaccharides are found in the cell walls of the bacteria, which live within the roots of the Echinacea plant.[1]

Furthermore, a much less easily quantified factor known as "faith" has a great role in determining whether or not an herb will work. There is the faith of the practitioner, who has selflessly used the herbs time and time again to help people regain good health. There is the faith of the patient, who must believe in his cure to give the herbs time to work. And, there is the faith of the grower who fills the herb with good intentions as it grows and with altruistic motivation keeps giving the plant what it needs to attain fruition. Faith is at least as important as chemistry in determining the results of the therapy. The combination of gentle chemistry and faith is a potent elixir,

and despite the recent proliferation of pharmaceutical drugs and modern medicine, whole herb therapy remains one of the most viable healing modalities in use worldwide.

Planning. When starting a new herb farm, herbal garden, or herbal landscape, it is best to first understand the land as it is (sun, soil, trees, water) and then grow herbs that will thrive in these conditions. If your garden is all shade, then think goldenseal, not sage. If you have only sun, then think oregano, not bloodroot. If you are located in northern California, grow yerba mansa and lomatium *(Lomatium dissectum),* not the circumpolar plants rhodiola and maralroot. So the point is, understand the habitat first and then proceed to grow plants that will flourish in your area.

---

[1]Pugh, N.D. et al. The majority of in vitro macrophage activation exhibited by extracts of some immune-enhancing botanicals is due to bacterial lipoproteins and lipopolysaccharides. International Immunopharmacology (2008) 8, 1023-1032

A Tour of Horizon Herbs Seed Farm. If you came here from over the mountain, you would drive on a winding, barely blacktopped road through mixed stands of second growth trees interspersed with clear cuts. The ascent would be made along open canyons with rushing water at their feet, patches of old growth, and many unkempt and potentially treacherous exits. You would navigate around piles of ancient crumbling rock, passing scrubby manzanita habitat, pine and hemlock, madrone and blue elderberry, chinquapin and cascara. Red-tailed hawks, bears, and mountain lions would probably see you at some point—even though you might not see *them*. In the winter, driving over this way would be impossible due to snow, but the rest of the year, this can be a wild and scenic drive. Oh, by the way, look out for logging trucks and wildly careening 4 x 4's (some of those hairpin turns leave little room for indiscretion). We live down from all that. It's tamer here—but not much.

Because of the full sun positioning of our land, even broken up as it is by intermittent natural tree cover and a cool riparian zone, we have planted in many trees. We plant trees from seed, of species of our choice, and in and amongst these medicinal trees, we have a working apple orchard planted in Arkansas native apple trees. In the spring, these are decked out with aromatic flowers that soon give way to green apples. By fall, the drooping sugary apples become a daily treat. During winter dormancy, we carefully prune back the twigs to make the trees ready for next year.

Several larger sections of land are left open for field growing of medicinals, but we don't have much room left, really. Being an avid collector of plants and a softy when it comes to our green friends, this place is plant dense to say the least. A visitor from Maui said "This is as close to the temperate tropics as any place could look."

There is a giant oak at the front gate that throws enough shadow for a long, twisting bed of nicely cared for skullcaps, snaking out

Bioregionalism. One practical approach is to find out from local people what was traditionally grown in the area and what is grown now. For example, in my own bioregion, from as early as 1875 all the way through to prohibition, hops was a major crop, grown on high wire trellises in the fertile soil of the river valleys. My lady's dad once worked in hops. I ended up making hops tincture when I was a manufacturing herbalist, and hops eventually became one of the most prolific and problem-free plants that I grow here on my little farm.

One bit of advice that I might tender to anyone moving onto new land or starting a new garden is to camp there overnight. Roll out your bedroll, lie back, listen, and watch. If you like what your senses tell you, then this bodes well for you and your new garden. To experience the rustlings of the plants in the night wind, to watch the moon course through the starry sky, and to experience the way the birds wake up in the morning is good medicine for you on the land.

from under the tree and dissolving into other species, running all the way across the field in careful groupings, ending up at the shelterbelt against the fence to the west. There are prominent gates, one with a maple leaf cutout in its wood and one with a wave pattern on its top board, gates leading to paths bringing you down the cut bank to the creek.

The creek flows throughout the year, in the summer slurring over slimy boulders, in the winter chattering whitewater, boulders scrubbed clean, periwinkles holding on beneath for dear life. There's a secret western garden under the shade of a maple that reaches her arms up from the yin-soaked streamside to clasp to her breast, like a yearning mother, a shade garden of her own making. We use green string to train wild yam vines into her branches. There are three ponds. Koi proliferate in bright orange and black schools in the main pond that is overhung by a willow.

The shadehouse beckons coolly, and from time to time we put on the misters there—whizzz. The tables in the shadehouse are suspended from the crossbeams, to give slugs and earwigs less of a leg up. The greenhouse steams and gets so hot by midsummer that we have to put a shade cloth over it, too, to avoid burning our young plants.

There are usually at least two smokin' large piles of washed cow manure on the land, one beside the rock fence out by the goat barn and one in the middle of the farm by the driveway. We aerate them by turning with shovels and we are known to run our rototiller into them. Blocks of coir are stacked in the shed next to a half-barrel, ready for hydration. A pile of white pumice reflects the sun like a beach. There's a big pile of coarse, sharp sand brought in from a local quarry (sand from a nearby river, really). There's a central "mixing trench" just wide enough for our rototiller, where we layer the ingredients for the potting soil and mix them all at once with a roar! There are several large carbon piles with protruding dead branches, and several more, carefully placed compost piles full of decomposing stems and piles of weeds. These sometimes let off a whiff of bacterial heat or a cabbagey odor of decomposition. There are undulating gardens with pathways, featured plants, and stone-encircled beds of plants.

The land features groupings of rock-lined "tortugas" (see Preparing the Ground—Chapter 15). There are what we call "floating islands" of nursery stock. These are potted shelterbelt trees in flats, resting upon generous amounts of red volcanic rock (cinders) and watered with creek water every couple of days during the growing season.

The permanent fields are full of rows and beds of mixed medicinals, including various weeds of our own introduction, interspersed with challenging patches of local blackberries and tough fescue grass. With this setup and the grace of the local weather, we grow a surprisingly wide array of herbs.

Our growing season is long—May through November. We tend to have frustratingly late springs, sunny and dry summer days tempered by cool nights, and usually experience a nice, toasty, late summer for maturing the crops. Because of the cold nights, our Swiss chard grows only about half as big as the plant would grow for someone gardening in a more humid climate, such as the Midwest. Although the first frost may arrive as early as the harvest moon in November, the flowers still bloom on and the seed harvest isn't complete until December, with *Artemisia annua,* eleuthero, skullcap, and persimmon being the last to mature.

We have a well that serves the water needs for our home, seed house, and nursery. The well water is good to drink. We have a pump in the creek that reaches the rest of the land by means of an extensive underground system of pipes. When it comes to the soil, if you can't keep it moist, bacteria and fungi won't want to live there. If bacteria and fungi don't want to live there, you don't have live soil, and if you don't have live soil, your plants are in trouble. So in the dry summer, it's really all about how to water the gardens at just the right intervals. Because the water belongs to everybody and all creatures, we use our water prudently. The plants drink, then we let the surface go dry. Now the plants push their roots down or down and out a little further. Then later we water again, deeply, and again we wait. Cloudy days may extend the intervals between waterings. Gardening is about the pauses. We apply compost, and later we see the results. We reap the benefits of patience, trusting in the goodness of natural things.

Here in the winter, water is thankfully not a problem. It comes from the sky as rain and it even snows a little. These events encourage winter activities, like sitting by the window with a cup of tea and staring out at the gray drizzle. There is introspection, yoga, music, art, writing, and carpentry. There is the joy and challenge of relationship, not just with loved ones, but with the whole interconnected web of being that one notices, acknowledges, and interacts with. Ultimately, the hunger of the birds is the same as our hunger.

Spring here is usually pretty wet, and nothing much needs watering until early June. Soon thereafter, watering becomes a big priority, and it all boils down to lots of twisting valves off and on, selective watering and night watering, set after set, moon cycle by moon cycle throughout the summer, while the leaves nearly crackle in turgid expansion and the crescent moon night owl hoots while you dance atop your own shadow avoiding a shivering shower of creek water.

Here in the summer, I spend days in the sun with shorts and no shirt, crawling up and down the field, knees caked, as hard as cow leather, crawling east to west and back again, along the rows, taking care of the plants one by one. Giving the knees a break, then, on the butt, crabbing along the rows, stopping and leaning forward to draw another dirt sun around another smiling plant, hands in full contact with the soil, cultivating the crust, foiling the plans of the weed seeds, feeling the swelling roots of my little charges. I am alone now with hair swinging, sweating, feeling alive.

Rubber fingers. If there was only one thing that I was allowed to give you, it would be a demonstration of this certain way to jiggle the fingers. It is a tactile movement of the wrists and fingers, back and forth, loose-wristed, rubber-fingered—a movement that serves in so many ways. Hold your hands out in front of you. Make the fingers as if you're about to give somebody a scalp massage. Now jiggle your hands back and forth, and keep your wrists flexible. If you raked your fingertips across a sandy surface doing this, they would leave the tracks of snakes. This movement, which I will in the future refer to as "rubber fingers," is a very useful technique, quintessential to the finesse of gardening.

When I'm holding a screen full of chaff and seeds, I find that this movement helps gently move the seeds on through the screen, separating the seeds from the chaff. It is the best way to even out the surface of the ground when I am composting or building raised beds, laying down layers of ingredients—sand, gravel, and mulch. Rubber fingers help distribute and shallowly bury seeds on the surface of a fine seedbed.

The healing touch. Go to the garden and put your fingers in the soil around a plant that you like. Jiggle your rubber fingers back and forth. Loosen up the soil around the plant and remove any stones or weeds from right around the stem. This will increase nutrient uptake and promote oxygen transfer around the roots. Hum a little tune to the plant, say mantras, or work with your mind in any way you know how in order to lessen the onslaught of discursive thoughts. This allows you to just *be* with that plant. Nurture it. Make circles around the plant with your fingers in the soil, and think about bringing in the sun energy, rain energy, and earth energy to the plant.

This work will make your hands very strong and tough. Your hands will rarely tire, as this movement is energizing to the whole system. This is the charged interface between our most highly tactile body aspect and the garden. It is a movement that gives much return sensation, because the sensory surface is in constant motion, leading to an increase in sensitivity, fine-tuning your work, doing it better.

Think about what good medicine the plant is, as it is, and as a medicinal herb, and how it's helping people now, and how it will help people when it offers itself up as a tea. Make the circles wider and wider, like a pebble thrown into still water, like a petroglyph on a rock in New Mexico, like the sun. Lean back on your heels and close your eyes for a minute or two and let the plant speak to you. This practice will bring you to a deeper understanding of your relationship to the biosphere. It will strengthen your connection to the medicine of the plants.

CHAPTER 14 — GROWTH CYCLES OF PLANTS

Annuals are plants that are sown from seed in the spring, mature in the fall, and don't over-winter. Borage, calendula, and Chinese balsam are annual flowers. These tend to be very easy to start from seed, and they respond well to direct-seeding in the flowerbed, tortuga, or field. Their seeds are generally fast-germinating, because the plant knows that it needs to get its grow going or it will be late for a very important date—the maturation of its seeds prior to the first frost!

Overwintering annuals (most references will call these "winter annuals") are plants that germinate in the late summer, creating a basal rosette that grows slowly through the fall and winter, and winters over (under the snow in some cases). In the spring, plants of this sort grow quickly from this established foundation and flower usually in the spring or early summer. The seeds then fall to the ground and sprout before the cold sets in. All this is accomplished within 12 months. Milk thistle, shepherd's purse, and California poppy are overwintering annuals. Matching the natural growth pattern (i.e. planting in the late summer for harvest the following spring) is a good way to grow these, because, in many cases, if you try planting overwintering annuals in the spring, they produce small individuals that go quickly to seed.

Herbaceous perennials are plants that produce only soft tissues (no wood), dying back down to the crown in the winter and rising up from the crown in the spring. Most medicinal herbs are herbaceous perennials, including the common European standbys, such as gipsywort, elecampane, and marshmallow. Many of our forest-dependent species also demonstrate this growth habit, including bloodroot, goldenseal, and ginseng.

The butterbur (*Petasites palmatus*) that grows wild in the creeks around where I live is a great example of an herbaceous perennial. The plants make a latticework of crisp, creeping rhizomes that course through the soft soil of the creek banks and even travel through the sand and gravel within the bed of the creek itself. Butterbur plants send up large, umbrella-shaped leaves in the spring, but these die completely back to the crown in the autumn.

Herbaceous perennials are best started from cuttings or from seed in the spring, but they are unlikely to make many flowers the first year. The main flowers appear in the spring or early summer of the second year and thereafter. A well-maintained patch of herbaceous perennials can be eternal.

Short-lived herbaceous perennials usually are most productive in their first and especially their second year of growth. The term "short-lived perennials" is not widely used, but I find it useful. Plants of this sort are winter-hardy, but tend to fade away, nonetheless, and usually disappear after growing for 2 or 3 years in the same place. Good examples are motherwort, feverfew, and Saint John's wort.

The parent plants fail when the older tissue rots away at the crown. Short-lived perennials are usually vigorous self-seeders, but you can also keep them strong by dividing the crown after the second year of growth (see Chapter 20 — Making Cuttings). Do this during the dormant period, in the late fall or early spring. Cut off any old stems, then dig the mother root and make cuts right down through the center of the crown. Pull it apart and divide the root into cuttings, making sure there is at least one bud and plenty of fine rootlets on each piece that will be replanted. Plant the divisions in good soil, roots down and buds up, and cultivate often until they re-establish themselves.

Woody perennials are herbs that make woody stems that remain above ground throughout the year. The plant may drop its leaves and create buds, but the woody portions do not die, instead providing a permanent framework for the next year's growth. The wood is bendable, not stiff and immutable like a tree. Lavender, heather, hyssop, rosemary, rue, southernwood, sage, and thyme are all woody perennials. These plants need fast-draining soil and full sun.

Woody perennials are normally planted from seed in the fall or early spring. The seed germinates as the ground warms up in the spring, and the seedlings soon attain their second set of true leaves. When this happens, they can be pricked into a gallon pot and then, when sufficiently sized up, transplanted to the field. In ideal circumstances or with very fast-growing species, this occurs in a month or two. When circumstances are less than ideal or with slower growing species, it may take until the spring of the second year before the woody perennials are ready to transplant out. In either case, they will probably put on long, branchy growth in the first summer, potentially giving rise to flowers in the fall.

In the fall of the first year, due to this leggy, adolescent growth, the woody perennials need to be cut back pretty far, say 6 or 8 inches above ground level. Cut back stronger on the lower, horizontal branches, and shape the rest of the plant into a dome. Use hand-held shears, hedge clippers, or, if you have many plants to cut back, use an electric or gas-powered hedge trimmer.

You will be especially glad that you did this when and if the snow falls. Woody perennials that have been properly cut back are much less likely to be damaged by snow inundation. The new growth emerges the following spring, creating a new, upwards curving branch that grows usually from the bud just below the cut.

Then in the second year, barring heavy fertilization, the plant doesn't put on so much growth. The wood that is produced is somewhat harder and denser, and it doesn't grow so fast. The second year is typified by a bounteous peak in flower production. In the fall of the second year, the normal rule of cutting back begins to apply—the new growth needs to be cut back to about 1 inch or at most 2 inches above the previous year's growth. This will assure that the plant does not become leggy and fall over, a potentially fatal occurrence.

In the ensuing years, you will notice that the properly trimmed plant becomes tamer, producing shorter wood, but maintaining even production of dependable quantities of flowers and seeds. Frequent weeding and cultivation, along with an occasional side-dressing of compost, colloidal rock phosphate, and sand helps maintain this yield.

Year in and year out it goes on this way, until the plant begins to age. For garden sage and rosemary, this is probably around year 10 or so. At this point, the sizing up of the plant reaches homeostasis. Once this balance is achieved, you will still have to trim off the dead flowers and seed heads on a yearly basis, but you will no longer have to cut back into the wood very much. If some of the branches die, remove them completely, and the lively stems will take over the gap. The plant will maintain a good, upright stance for a few more years. At age 15 or so, it will probably begin to erode out from the base, the older, woody stems tiredly reclining, decomposing back into the soil from which they came. So you see, the job of cutting back really changes according to the age of the plant.

Once the base of the plant begins to decompose and the yield shrinks, then it is time to say goodbye. The tough, somewhat spongy wood is always a challenge to rip from the earth. Sometimes it helps to chant, "Matter is neither created nor destroyed, only transformed," while doing this. You'll develop your own technique, but remember what the dentist said—don't grind your teeth!

Biennials are herbs that live for 2 growing seasons. They are monocarpic, meaning that once they flower and make seed, they die. However, plants of this sort are usually very powerful self-seeders, and they are famously easy to grow from seed. In established populations, it isn't unusual to be able to find seedlings, first-year rosettes, and flowering or seeding individuals, all at the same time and growing in concert.

When the seed of a biennial is planted in the spring, the plant first produces a large basal rosette. In the fall of the first year, this rosette either dies back down to the crown or remains evergreen through the winter. The plant then overwinters and in the spring produces a leafy, basal rosette, that gives rise to flowering stalks, which go rapidly to flower and then to seed. This usually occurs in the late spring or early summer. A few good examples of plants that follow this pattern of growth are angelica, burdock, dang-gui, evening primrose, and mullein.

The life expectancy of biennials may be extended by cutting back the flowering stalk as soon as it starts to form. This also encourages the production of larger roots, as the energy of the plant is forced down into the root once again. This method may be used in the production of angelica root, in which case the plant may be grown for 2 full seasons, and the root harvested in the fall of the second year. It can feel a bit cruel to cut back the flowering stalk, though, because the plant has been waiting so long to express itself, and cutting it back foils the reproductive imperative.

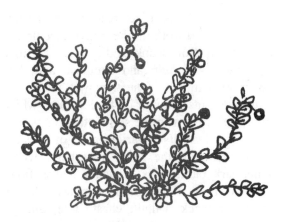

Vines are powerfully vigorous and flexible, but they lack the ability to hold themselves up, instead relying on other plants or the trellis for support. Vines twist and twine around things to hold on. Vines can be classed as drapers (which remain quite close to the ground, like jiao-gu-lan) and climbers (which will go as high as the trellis allows, like grapes). They can be herbaceous or woody. Some good examples of herbal vines are: codonopsis, gelsemium, and passionflower.

Evergreens are herbs that may be soft-tissued or woody, but in either case do not die back to the ground, instead retaining their leaves throughout the growing season and the winter. Evergreens are generally available to harvest for medicine at any time of year, are excellent choices for landscaping and bedding, and can provide pleasant color during the dreary wintertime. A few good examples are: false unicorn (*Chamaelirium luteum*), horny goat weed (*Epimedium* spp.), manzanita, Oregon grape, uva ursi, and wintergreen. These plants can be extremely long-lived.

Shrubs are low-lying woody perennials that aspire to be trees, but usually have softer wood, multiple stems, and a squat habit. For these reasons, they have difficulty attaining tree status. Shrubs, like trees, may be deciduous or evergreen. A few good examples are: black currant, cramp bark, forsythia, gardenia, and roses. What differentiates shrubs from woody perennials is that the shrubs tend to be larger and woodier. The main method of upkeep is to remove weeds from under the plant and mulch, or alternatively to maintain the grasses under the shrub by mowing up close. Shrubs can be encouraged to grow to their full potential by pruning out the smaller stems. Cut them off at the base. Rows of shrubs can be shaped into hedges, making a natural barrier that is sometimes easier to upkeep than a fence, and usually a great deal more handsome.

Trees are trees. They tend to have single stems that will show, in cross section, the corky pith at the center, then the hard and heavy heartwood, then the softer sapwood, surrounded by the inner bark and the outer bark.

For the most part, it is best to plant trees directly in the native soil, without adding any compost or soil amendments. They tend to respond better this way. If you put compost in the hole before planting the tree, then the taproots will not want to delve into the harder soil beneath. They will be like a late sleeper, unwilling to crawl out from under the blankets.

If you want to fertilize trees, the preferable technique is to work up the soil surface underneath them, from trunk to drip line. Fertilize this zone with kelp and compost, and then cover with mulch. The tree will absorb the extra nutrients through its feeder roots, which are most active near the soil surface.

In herbalism, various parts of trees are used, including the roots, root bark, wood, inner bark, bark, twigs, branches, leaves, flowers, and fruits. Some good examples of herbal trees are black walnut, chaste tree, ginkgo, juniper, and hawthorn. Where would we be without the trees?

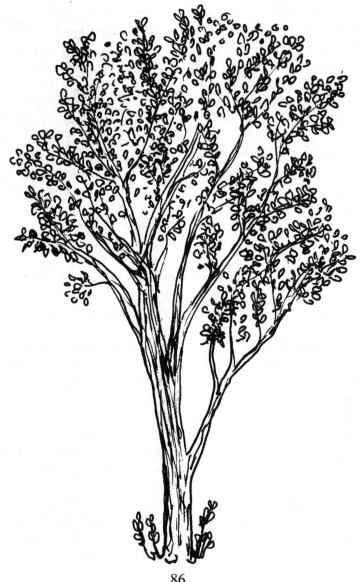

CHAPTER 15 — PREPARING THE GROUND

Plants are accumulators. The kind, quality, and quantity of soil substrate, nutrients, sun, and water that are available during the growing phase strongly influence the food value of garden vegetables and the medicinal value of medicinal herbs. Although most herbs do not require the kind of highly fertile soil that garden vegetables need, they do require living soils that contain bacteria, fungi, and have a structure that holds water, but also allows excess water to drain away. In areas where the soil meets this description, a little compost, banded below the plants at transplant or side-dressed around their crowns during the growing season, is usually all they need to live their lives fully and give dependable yields of good medicine.

Often, fallow lands that were once in production can be readily resuscitated. The ground is first tilled, then allowed to rest for 1 or 2 weeks to give any vegetable residue time to compost in. Then the soil may be fertilized with a little chicken manure or crab waste, and tilled again before planting seeds or setting out transplants. I call these first-year gardens, and they are usually highly productive and trouble-free. In the second year, some further method of building fertility and replenishing the land, such as composting and cover-cropping, will probably be necessary.

Cover-cropping is a way of growing fertility in situ without having to bring in too many materials from far away. Whether the land has been recently in production or has been allowed to lie fallow for some time, cover-cropping is a great way to rebuild the soil. Fall-planted cover crops protect the soil through the harsh winter. Spring-planted cover crops make use of natural precipitation and warm conditions to produce a quick, green blanket over the ground. The advantages of cover-cropping include: building soil by fixing nitrogen and increasing carbon (biomass); improving habitat for beneficial organisms (bacteria, fungi, earthworms, and pollinators), while forcing out weeds and harmful pests; bringing up minerals and nutrients from deep within the earth; aerating the soil and subsoil; improving water retentiveness; beauty; edibility; and medicinality!

Preparing the ground. The method is simple: mow, whip, disc, or otherwise mulch up the existing cover (usually consisting of grasses, weeds, and crop residues). Do this when the ground is neither too wet nor too dry, so you can work the soil without damaging it. Prepare the seedbed by disking, harrowing, or roto-tilling. A rough seedbed is usually all that is required, especially since making multiple

passes with a tiller in order to break up more clods can reduce the carbon content of the soil. Plowing may be indicated if there is a very thick thatch of grass roots, but is generally best avoided, as it tends to disrupt the soil strata. If your garden is small or set up in raised beds, simply pull the weeds by hand or mow it close with a lawn mower, then break up the surface with a garden fork and rake it level.

Sowing cover crop seed. Strew the cover crop seed on the soil, rake it in shallowly, then tamp the surface and water (or wait for rain). When the cover crop is still relatively short (6 to 12 inches or so), it will have achieved its highest nitrogen content. At this point (unless it is fall and you want the cover crop to blanket the winter garden), mow it down, let it decompose for a few days, then fork, till, or disc the residue back into the earth. Even on poor land, after a single round of cover-cropping, the soil structure and fertility will be noticeably improved.

If soil fertility is poor, it is always a good idea to scatter a little chicken manure or compost on the land just before strewing and raking in the cover crop seed. This will give the plants something to get going on and will avert the failure that sometimes occurs when the cover crop seed simply doesn't have enough nutrients available for establishment. I see it as a change of state—the nitrogen exists in the chicken waste, is absorbed into the body of the plant, and eventually dissolves back into the soil again. In order to complete the cycle, all we really need is a pea seedling and a naughty hen to peck it up!

Oats and peas mix. The most classic of all cover crops is composed of equal weights of oats and peas, which are classified as annuals or over-wintering annuals. The peas fix atmospheric nitrogen in nodules on their roots. The tall, rigid, straight stems of the oats are composed of carbon. The oats are nourished by the peas and, in return, give the peas a trellis to climb up on. This is a living yin-yang symbol that cannot really be improved upon as cover crops go. It is the best all-around choice, as it contains, in green form, equal parts of the same elements that make compost work.

In warm winter areas (10° F or warmer), the oats and peas are planted in the fall for quick germination and winter cover, then cut back and turned under in the spring. In cold winter areas (10° F and colder), it is best to wait until early spring to plant, in which case the crop will reach maturity within a single growing season. Sow 3 lbs. per 1,000 square feet or 60 lbs. per acre.

Crimson clover (*Trifolium incarnatum*) is an annual cover crop that gives rise to myriads of truly luxurious, upright blossoms, swollen at the base and pointed at the top. They are indeed a very dark shade of crimson, but regrettably the flowering period is a short 2 weeks. You have to appreciate it quickly, and then mow it down!

Those living in warmer climates do well to sow in the fall, while in areas with winter temperatures that dip below 5° F, spring planting is preferred. Crimsom clover is a good plant to under-sow into the corn patch. When the corn is knee-high and has been thinned, weeded, cultivated, and fertilized, then come in with the crimson clover seed and strew it between the rows of corn. Now, the crimson clover will come up thickly and it will force out the pigweeds, so you won't have to weed again, and it will nourish the corn plants as they mature, resulting in big yields of heavy cobs. Then, after you harvest the corn, cut back the stalks and feed them to the cows or the goats or the compost pile or just let them fall back to the earth, and the crimson clover will cover over the debris and make flowers.

Crimson clover is famous for producing a dense, monotypic stand that discourages growth of weedy species. A solid cover crop of crimson clover will fix 150 lbs. of pure nitrogen per acre by way of nitrogen nodules on the roots, and the aerial parts of the plant are rich in carbon and help build soil. Inoculate and sow 1 lb. per 1000 square feet or 20 lbs. per acre.

Red clover (*Trifolium pratense*) is the next most useful cover crop, a multipurpose perennial that flowers usually in the second year. The roots are good excavators and break up hardpan. The plant is less spreading than white clover. Once cut back and tilled under, red clover does not tend to persist (although it may self-seed if conditions are right).

Red clover will fix about 140 lbs. of nitrogen per acre, as long as bacterial rhizobia are present in the soil. The rhizobia induce nitrogen-fixing nodules to grow on the roots of the leguminous cover crops, and when these nodules break down in the soil, they make nitrogen available to the subsequent planting. When sowing clovers as a cover to existing gardens, it is not necessary to use rhizobium inoculant, because rhizobia will already be present in the soil. However, if working with fallow pastureland or lawns, it makes sense to inoculate the seed.

Rhizobium inoculant is widely available from the same places where you buy cover crop seed. Pour the seed in a bucket, add a few drops of water and stir to moisten, then add the powdered inoculant, stir to coat the seed, and then plant. Some seeds are precoated with inoculant, which is just fine. Sow 1/2 lb. per 1,000 square feet or 10 lbs. per acre.

Fenugreek (*Trigonella foenum-graecum*) is an annual legume that is native to the Mediterranean and hardy to 10° F. The plants have aromatic foliage bearing white flowers with distinctive blue markings, giving way to the very long, follicular pods. Fenugreek breaks up heavy clay soils and contributes nitrogen and organic matter. Direct-seed in late summer, fall, or early spring. The seed germinates well in cold soils. Sow 2 lbs. per 1000 square feet or 40 lbs. per acre.

Fava beans and bell beans (both classified as *Vicia faba*) are nitrogen-fixing legumes related to vetch. Unlike vetch, they remain upright (not viney), are easily controlled, and are not particularly strong self-seeders. The plants have fragrant black and white flowers that attract beneficial insects, and their deep root systems break up hardpan. They fix about 150 lbs. of nitrogen per acre. The seed is large and does best when sowed 2 inches deep. Sow in late summer or spring. Inoculate and sow at 5 lbs. per 1,000 square feet or 175 lbs. per acre.

Annual ryegrass (*Lolium multiflorum*) is an annual grass that is an ideal choice for sowing on pathways between beds of herbs, because it produces a quick, green lawn, which is impermanent and noninvasive. The seed germinates and grows quickly in cold soils and poor soils, forces out weeds, and stabilizes the soil with its extensive, spreading root system. Sow in the fall or spring at 1/2 lb. per 1,000 square feet or 10 lbs. per acre.

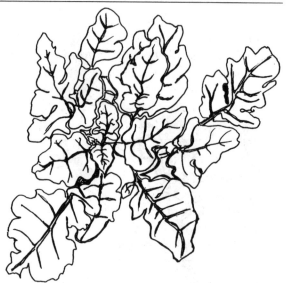

Black mustard (*Brassica nigra*) is an annual or overwintering annual. Although the plant does not fix atmospheric nitrogen, it does sequester nitrogen from the soil, which is then returned to the soil in a more bioavailable form when the plants senesce or are cut back and tilled in. Black mustard is allelopathic, effectively inhibiting growth of weeds when it is thickly sown. The plant inhibits infestations of aphids and spider mites and is therefore usefully employed as an understory plant in orchards. In cold regions where fall-sown mustard winter-kills, the decomposed plants make a desirable mulch for growing spring vegetables. Mustard thrives in regular garden soil and withstands heavy or clay soils. In warmer winter areas (above 20° F), mustard may be sown from fall all the way through to early spring. In cold winter areas, it may be sown as a quick cover in the fall or as an early spring crop. Sow 1/4 lb. per 1,000 square feet or 5 lbs. per acre.

Buckwheat (*Fagopyron esculentum*) is a nonleguminous broadleaf loaded with bio-flavonoids, but not a nitrogen-fixer. The plant germinates and grows well in warm soils, so it is really the best choice for a quick summer cover crop. Growing to maturity in 50 days, buckwheat can be an effective follow-up after summer harvests (burdock root, calendula flowers), then turned under in the late summer or fall. The plant produces a great deal of very quickly compostable organic matter, improves bioavailability of phosphorus in the soil, and forces out summer weeds. Buckwheat is a good trap crop for thrips, which are minute sucking insects that feed on plant juices and may otherwise take up residence on fruit trees, grape vines, or medicinal herbs. Thrips are also disease vectors, and when present in large numbers are known to reduce plant vitality. Buckwheat flowers also attract beneficial insects and pollinators. Sow 3 lbs. per 1,000 square feet or 60 lbs. per acre.

Daikon (*Raphanus sativus*) is a biennial radish that quickly produces an extremely long and strong taproot. This is not a nitrogen fixer, but can be sown along with red clover or other nitrogen-fixing cover crops in order to improve breakup of hardpan. The root can easily excavate to a depth of 18 inches and, when it dies back, this excavation becomes filled with organic matter that oxygenates the subsoil and improves vitality of subsequent crops. Sow in fall or early spring at 1 lb. per 1,000 square feet or 20 lbs. per acre.

the stalks are tilled back into the land, this material increases the organic content, and especially water-holding capacity, of the soil. Under-sowing the half-grown sunflowers with crimson clover provides an added element of nitrogen fixation, and this dynamic duo can quickly replenish depleted soils.

Sunflower (*Helianthus annuus*) is a summer crop that produces a great deal of food energy for humans and birds. It is best to band a little compost or chicken manure under the row at planting, and cultivate and side-dress with more manure when the plants are a few weeks old. Mature sunflowers constitute a prodigious carbon resource that eventually takes the form of friable stalks and a spongy core. Once

Alfalfa (*Medicago sativa*) is a perennial cover crop that does best in areas of high fertility with plenty of water availability. It is hardy to all zones. The herb is well-adapted for use in the field, garden, shelterbelt, and between trees in the orchard. It can be mowed and will regrow, leaving behind up to 10 tons of organic matter per acre. The roots are very deeply delving, fixing up to 200 lbs. of nitrogen per acre and sequestering subsurface minerals. The sprouts of alfalfa are a rich source of chlorophyll. Sow 1 lb. per 1,000 square feet or 20 lbs per acre.

THE TORTUGA

Advantages of the tortuga. The tortuga is a glorified raised bed technique that we have stumbled upon here at Horizon Herbs farm. The tortuga may be used to create plant habitat in tight spaces, up next to buildings, or in problem areas. This is a powerful technique for feeding, watering, and protecting plants, lending itself handily to the creation of specific econiches for rare and unusual herbs.

The tortuga is composed of thick strata of mineral and organic ingredients layered on top of a strong weed barrier. We all know that it is cheaper and more efficient to "grow your soil" with the cover crop method, but this takes time and is not always a realistic option. Farm-derived or imported soil ingredients used in the tortuga (such as compost, micronutrients, sand, coir, and pumice) give the advantage of fast drainage, are rich in nutrients, and are usually free of weed seeds. The walls of the tortuga are made up of cement blocks, which are thrifty, inexpensive, and easy to lay, or natural rocks, which are functional and aesthetically pleasing, or a combination of the two.

The first beds I built this way resembled giant turtles (*tortuga* is Spanish for turtle), and thus the name was born. The tortuga may actually be shaped any way you like—it doesn't have to look like a turtle. Making the beds correspond to the contours of the land or designing them in other natural shapes (such as leaves, clouds, or sinuous lines) blends them with the landscape and makes the plants happy.

The tortuga can be made impervious to gophers and other burrowers, as well as sweet peas, blackberries, poison oak, and other tenacious weeds. The rock around the edge serves as a solar collector, radiating heat at night. This protects young plants from frost and extends the harvest window.

Soil ingredients, such as coir, peat, or compost, are extremely hydrophilic and will support plants through times of drought. Compost and micronutrients produce plants of heightened mineral content and improve overall yield of roots, leaves, and seeds. This technique results in vegetables that are rich in food value and herbs that harbor high concentrations of medicinal compounds.

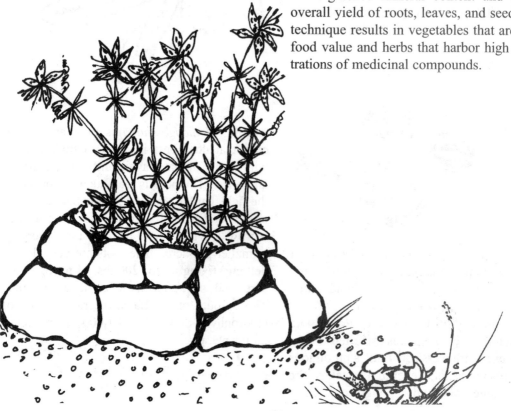

Laying down and securing the weed barrier. First, lay down a water-permeable weed barrier. Weed barriers range from the recycled (multiple layers of used cardboard without staples or tape), to the organic (coir matting, which consists of long-fiber coir adhered with natural latex) to the industrial strength (polypropylene weed barrier that can be purchased at your local nursery). Do not use plastic, as it is extremely important for oxygen and water to be able to percolate up and down through the weed barrier. Plastic will spell trouble in the form of root-rot. If only fighting weeds, recycled cardboard is the best choice. If gophers or ground squirrels are an issue, then use 1/2-inch mesh hardware cloth or very strong polypropylene weed barrier.

Cut or piece the weed barrier into the shape of the bed. Make the footprint of the weed barrier 2 feet bigger than the bed will eventually be. Now put a 4-inch thick layer of fast-draining materials, such as: sand, cinders, pea gravel, a gravel-sand mix, or volcanic pumice, on top of the weed barrier and spread it evenly out over the edges until it blends smoothly into the surrounding land.

Building up the walls. Then lay a course of cement blocks or stones all the way around the outside of the bed, 2 feet in from the edge. Once you encircle your bed with rock, you have defined the 2 significant areas—the outer access to the bed and the inner bed itself. The "bib" of weed barrier covered with the fast-draining material that now runs all the way around the bed will keep the weeds back.

Bulk the bib with more sand, covering up any view of the first layer of rock or concrete block that is showing from the outside. If you lay it tight, then rodents will have a hard time getting into the bed. If there is plentiful local stone, use this, but if stone is dearly had, then use the cement blocks or a combination of blocks and decorative stone. This will give the tortuga very high sides, which you want— the deeper the better. Ideally, the walls will measure 18 inches deep, from the rim of the top rock down to the weed barrier.

Filling the tortuga. Fill the bed space with thick layers of coir, sand, nitrogen-rich compost, pumice or pea gravel. Finish with a coir mulch, more compost, or more sand, depending on what you decide to grow there. Make each layer at least 4 inches deep. Be generous with all the ingredients. If possible, bring them in by the truckload. We combine micronutrients (rock powders and kelp) with the compost layer. The layers are not mixed, but rather left in strata.

By choosing the right soil ingredients, it is possible to tailor the soil to the plants. For instance, you would make thick layers of predominantly organic ingredients if planting yacon, but sand and pumice would make habitat for white sage.

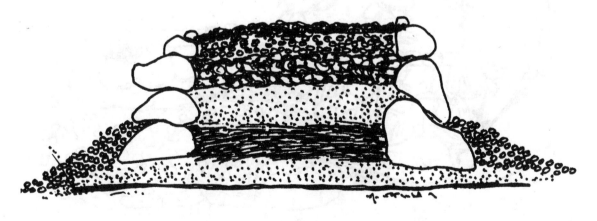

Planting the tortuga. According to our observations, different plants will develop root, tuber, and rhizome structures in various strata (mineral vs. organic). Plants that have spreading roots (e.g. gotu kola or spilanthes) are best planted in the layers of soil above the weed barrier, while plants with deep taproots (e.g. pleurisy root or poke) can be planted through the weed barrier into the mineral soil below. To plant through the weed barrier, use a sharp spade—pierce through all the soil layers, then through the weed barrier, and give the roots of your plant access to the soil that lies underneath the weed barrier.

The loose soils of the tortuga provide little resistance to the spread of stolonaceous plants. This means that if you plant arnica, bugleweed, Chinese lantern, grasses, yerba mansa, skullcap, or other vigorous creepers in a tortuga, you must be prepared for these plants to fill the bed from rim to rim! Plants that make spreading crowns like lady's mantle, meadowsweet, and blue vervain will also tend to spread joyfully through the friable soils of the tortuga. Woody perennials that have stolonaceous habit (e.g. angelica tree) will also send up many new sprouts in the tortuga. Taprooted plants (e.g. lovage or parsley) will be more likely to stay put, although you can be sure they will attain a great size!

Maintaining the tortuga. A tortuga is somewhat protected and permanent, in that it cannot easily be walked on or overcome by weeds. The small amount of weeding needed within such a feature is more fun than work. The hydrophilic organic ingredients (compost and coir) maintain moisture between waterings and through drought. The sand and pumice promote perfect drainage, which is appreciated by most plants. The stones store heat during the day and release it to the plants at night, resulting in early crops and exceedingly large and healthy individuals.

To maintain the integrity of the tortuga as grasses and weeds begin to interlope from outside, you're going to have to trim, weed whip, or mow up to the rock wall from the outside. This provides a clear margin around the rock wall. The spreading arms of plants originating from the tortuga will eventually express themselves into this space.

Early in the spring, comb over the surface of the tortuga with your fingers, removing the weeds and locating the emerging perennials. Now, generously side-dress compost around the perennials. This will help keep the soil level topped up, and the tortuga will last for a very long time. After all, turtles are quite long-lived!

CHAPTER 16 — THE GREENHOUSE AND THE SHADEHOUSE

Standard greenhouse technique. The value of a greenhouse is in extending the seasons while providing greater control. Greenhouses are useful for producing seedlings of both annuals and perennials. The standard greenhouse technique is to start by filling a container (such as a gallon pot) with hand-made potting soil, sprinkle plenty of seed on the surface of the soil, then cover with a very thin layer of potting soil, no thicker than the thickness of the seed itself (more in Chapter 19 — Planting Seeds). This is the default method that will work well for about 50% of temperate species.

Much care must be exercised in watering, lest cold, moist conditions contribute to damping-off disease among the seedlings (this makes them keel over and die). For the most part it is best to water once daily, allowing the soil surface to dry slightly before watering again. Water gently, so as not to dislodge the seeds. (You are a gentle summer rain.) The soil will hydrate, swell, and hold the seed in place. Do not cover with plastic. Seedlings are thinned in the pot or flat when they attain one set of true leaves and are pricked out (transplanted) to larger pots only when they attain two sets of true leaves. Transplant into quart or gallon size pots.

Within a few days after pricking the seedlings to their new pots, they ought to respond nicely to the warmth and good light. Now, using your fingers, cultivate gently around the firm, young stem of each plant. This serves to aerate the roots, increases the flow of nutrition to the plant, and also rejuvenates the connection between you and the plant. If the greenhouse is warm and there is good light, then the plants will grow.

If the plants begin to appear yellow or are very slow to develop, it's probably either because of a drainage problem or because of a lack of nutrients. Squishily spongy soil that smells malodorously is a sign of poor drainage. Replace the surface soil with pure sand, repot the plant in lighter soil, and/or move the flat to a warmer and dryer location. If the drainage looks OK, then more nutrients are probably required. Side-dress with compost, worm castings, or kelp.

My friend Erich discovered that during the colder months, a tea made with fresh milk thistle rosettes or other greenery can bolster the plants along in their dormancy without over-stimulating them. During warmer months, a tea made with comfrey leaf, worm castings, or kelp may prove very useful for watering in seeds, watering plants, or foliar-feeding adult plants, both potted and in the garden.

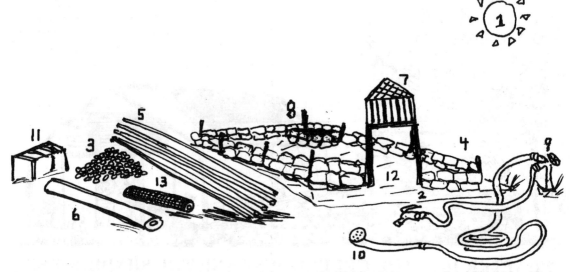

Building your greenhouse. Following find a few of the basic practices that I've found most helpful in building and maintaining the solar greenhouse:

1) Locate on the sunniest spot on the land. Situate facing south so as to take best advantage of the sun. Angle glazing toward the sun.

2) Make sure to lay down a weed barrier to keep the inside weed-free. Weed barriers must allow water to percolate down through.

3) Use gravel floors to provide fast drainage. Pea gravel or river pebbles are preferable to crushed rock, as they provide superior drainage and are kinder to the feet.

4) Build a heavy foundation out of rocks or blocks and make sure that the uprights of the framework are very sturdily attached to it.

5) Build a framework out of metal pipe, poly pipe, or wood, designed to carry your glazing and resilient enough to withstand wind stress.

6) Glazing options include UV-resistant plastic sheeting (good for about 6 years), twinwall polycarbonate (good for about 20 years), and glass (good until it breaks). Install glazing so as to sheet water off of the framework.

7) Ventilation is critical. Electric fans are costly, but effective. The electricity-free method is to provide vents at the peak to let out hot air, and wide doors or rollup sides to let in fresh air.

8) Plan to enclose a small pond inside the greenhouse. This will provide solar mass, a source of warm water for watering plants, on-site frog production, habitat for water plants, and beauty.

9) Make sure there is easy access to water, including a good garden hose for washing up.

10) Irrigation. Hand-water with a watering wand attached to the hose, or set up overhead misters to water the flats.

11) Keep the flats up off the floor with concrete blocks or slatted tables.

12) Design for easy human access. Central aisles usually measure 4 to 6 feet wide to allow for passage of a wheelbarrow. Leave 3-foot aisles between beds or tables. Beds or tables that can be accessed from both sides usually measure 4 feet wide. Beds or tables that can be accessed from only one side usually measure no greater than 30 inches wide.

13) Plan to cover the greenhouse with 40% shade cloth during the summer, to prevent the plants from being scorched. Remove the shade cloth in the fall before winter snows become imminent, otherwise the shade cloth will prohibit snow from sloughing off the greenhouse, and even the most sturdily built structure can collapse under the snow load.

It is good to keep in mind that every layer of glazing also produces 15% of shade (even though you can't see it). A single layer of glazing is sufficient for the purposes of: season extension, avoiding early and late frosts, starting seeds, cultivating seedlings, and growing greens for the kitchen table. Another great use of such a greenhouse is to keep a section of mother plants in beds or in gallon or larger pots. These are choice plants that may be planted out for seed production or may be maintained as a source of root or stem cuttings, for the purpose of increase.

Glazing the greenhouse with 2 layers will reduce the total sunlight by 30%, while providing a great deal of insulation value. A greenhouse such as this can be made even more effective by providing solar mass. This consists of the concrete foundation of the greenhouse itself, the gravel floor, the pond, permanent beds lined with concrete block and/or natural stone, the soil within these beds, or any other means of heat storage that can be devised. If the temperature can be maintained at 60° F or higher, then this could be called a "tropical greenhouse." The temperatures within such a structure can easily exceed 100° F on a hot day. Having openings to ventilate the peak, as well as large door openings, is very important.

Creating zones within greenhouses. One of the distinct advantages of greenhousing is the abundance of free natural light that arrives for the benefit of the plants. In a natural greenhouse, the light ray arrives directly from the sun, pierces through the clear glazing, and is then trapped within, bouncing around and doing good things for the plants.

If the greenhouse is big enough, the inside can be divided up into beds or tables containing plants from various ecological zones. For instance, the cacti can all be located on the south side, perhaps in gallon pots on a table. The cacti can be cared for by weeding and applying pure sand or pumice around the plants. They can be watered very infrequently.

Another zone would be the area around the pond, where the temperature is modulated by the water and there is good humidity available. I use an area of this sort for growing plants from the southern states that like it hot and humid, for example wild job's tears (*Onosmodium virginianum*). Building an additional plastic room within the greenhouse may allow for production of orchids and other tropical plants. An area of this sort may require humidification with misters and heating during the winter. Another area might be designed for the efficient planting of herb and vegetable seeds and for the potting up of transplants and cuttings. Working with the flats up on a workbench allows for expansive posture and can save your back.

In all, having different zones within the greenhouse helps mix up the indoor ecology, providing a certain amount of resiliency toward common greenhouse pests, such as aphids and white fly. Of course, common sense tells us that good sanitary practices, such as: washing out the pots, keeping soil up off the ground, picking up boards or other debris that might have been left lying around, trimming dead growth off of the older plants, and the inevitable weeding and disposal of weeds, all contribute to keeping the greenhouse alive and healthy.

Standard shadehouse technique. Next to the outdoor nursery bed and the greenhouse, the shadehouse is equally useful for working up medicinals. This is an ideal spot for gently propagating the remaining 50% of temperate species that do *not* do well in a greenhouse.

Building the shadehouse. To build a shadehouse, put down a weed barrier, cover with gravel or volcanic cinders, build an overhead framework, and cover with 60% shade cloth. Drip lines fitted with misters can be attached to the underside of the framework, in order to allow for gentle, cooling watering without much labor input. Flats of plants are then situated on tables or on concrete blocks.

Once you have a shadehouse, you will truly wonder how you ever managed without one. Ours is in continuous use. Many seeds are planted here. When we transplant into pots, we often put the seedlings in the shadehouse for a few days to recuperate. When we make cuttings and pot them up, we keep them in the shadehouse until they make roots. I've often anthropomorphically described this as my "plant spa," because most any plant that seems to be suffering can be left in the shade and pampered for awhile until it comes back to vibrancy.

This is also a primary spot for sowing seeds that require cool temperatures and even moisture for germination (e.g. echinacea). Shade-dependent herbs, such as Chinese coptis, false unicorn (*Chamaelirium luteum*), goldenseal, wild yam, black cohosh, blue cohosh, and bloodroot germinate best in the forest or in the shadehouse. I find that the even temperatures and moist shade are crucial for germinating and working up many rare and unusual plants, such as: Himalayan mayapple (*Podophyllum hexandrum*) Indian valerian (*Valeriana jatamansii*), mandrake (*Mandragora officinalis*), and osha (*Ligusticum porteri*). I've used the shadehouse for growing local lilies and trillium from seed, holding flats in ideal conditions for 3 years before these double-dormant and 2-phase germinators show their first delicate leaves.

In the shadehouse, flats and potted plants are likely to support growth of bryophytic mosses, liverworts, and hornworts that may tend to asphyxiate your seeds and plants. To maintain good conditions, remove and discard the moss and spread new mulch on the surface. Coir mixed with sand is a very effective top dressing that resists the mosses. When flats of long-germinating seeds are overcome by mosses, it can be quite a trick to replace the mulch without disturbing the quiescent seeds, but this is exactly what must be done.

When the flats of germinating seeds and the potted plants are properly weeded and watered, the protection, organization, and control afforded by the shadehouse increases success rates substantially. Long-germinating seeds germinate, and forest plants thrive, flower, and fruit.

The shadehouse is an excellent place to work during the hotter parts of the day. Sensitive tasks like transplanting bareroot seedlings and propagation from cuttings can be accomplished without drying out the roots (or the gardener, for that matter) in the relentless noontide sun. If it is really hot, one might even turn on the misters, a cool respite from the heat of August.

CHAPTER 17 — COMPOST

Power of compost. I believe strongly in the power of compost. This is the substance that defines the organic garden and greenhouse. Compost is wonderfully spongy and hydrophilic, so it improves texture and water-holding capacity, while serving as a fungal and bacterial inoculant that vitalizes the soil and feeds the plants. The quality of the cultivated herb is directly related to the quality of the compost used to grow it.

Using compost to grow medicinal herbs. Applying compost will improve the health, growth, and yield of most medicinal herb crops. Compost improves the nutrient content of garden vegetables, and the production of secondary compounds in most medicinal herbs is augmented by the use of compost.

However, I think a reasonable argument can be made for not using too much compost in the production of certain medicinal herbs. Adult perennial essential-oil-bearing plants, such as: sage, rosemary, thyme, and hyssop, probably ought not be given too much compost, which may stimulate fast growth of green aerial portions to the detriment of essential-oil content.

Spring ephemerals, such as goldenseal and bloodroot, thrive when given composted *forest* products, but abhor composted *manure*. My experiments have shown that *Ephedra* species do poorly when given compost. Woody perennials, such as ginkgo trees and many other medicinal trees, ought not be given compost in their planting holes, although it is fine to spread compost underneath the trees where the feeder roots can absorb the extra nutrients. Such applications are best made in the spring, since composting feeder roots late in the summer stimulates fast-growing wood studded with soft buds that can be easily damaged by winter cold. Finally, since alkaloids are nitrogen-based molecules, alkaloid production of low-dose botanicals (such as lobelia) can be overstimulated by application of composts high in nitrogen.

Location. Compost piles are best situated near the garden, in close proximity to the source of many of the ingredients. You want to be able to reach the pile easily with a forkful of weeds. These piles of soft vegetal matter are composted down best when they are turned frequently, so it is best to locate them close by, so they cannot be forgotten. Piles of very woody debris, however, are best located far from the garden, because they may harbor slugs, they take years to break down, and may tend to get in the way. These piles are best located in the shade of the woods, where they will stay moister and are readily colonized by fungi.

Compost or composted manure? More than anything, the availability of ingredients for making good compost will determine how many plants you can effectively grow. Therefore, it makes sense to throw all compostables onto the pile. Vegetarian compost is made out of layers of carbon (usually colored brown) and nitrogen-rich (usually colored green) ingredients. Vegetarian compost is the preferred application for woody perennials. Composted manure is generally made by layering manure with straw and is best for applying to leafy herbs and vegetables. You will probably want to make both kinds of compost for your use, using ingredients on hand or ingredients obtained from local dairies, ranches, or farms.

The carbon pile. This is really the core principle of natural gardening. Every piece of woody debris and every blade of grass are significant in supporting the interconnected health of plants and other life forms, from earthworm to *Homo sapiens,* on the land. The best way to recycle these ingredients is by piling them up. The piles really break down into two classes: woody debris and soft debris.

Woody debris is composed mostly of tree limbs too small to cut for firewood. The woody pile always gets a big boost when the fruit trees are pruned in the winter. Be bold about it—you don't have to feel ashamed of your pile as it grows bigger with all the things you find to add to it—branches from that ash tree that fell down on the eastern fence line, prunings from the peach tree, more prunings from the hawthorn tree, and half-rotten boards from a wooden flat no longer useable. Such a pile may look unkempt to the uninitiated, but the songbirds don't care about that—they will use the interlocking interstices of the pile to protect themselves from predators. The frogs won't mind, either. They'll overwinter underneath the pile, staying warm and moist within the rotting wood.

Over the years, as you add more to it, the pile will grow larger, and this is good, because the larger it is, the more likely it will be to reach the critical mass for efficient decomposition. In fact, it's so worthwhile to grow the pile bigger, that it often makes sense to walk your raw debris further and make bigger piles, instead of opting for many smaller piles, even though the latter arrangement might seem a bit more convenient. On the outside, the wood in the pile may be still green, but at the core, the wood is breaking down and rotting into pure humus.

This is not only a good method for harmlessly recycling debris in open, sunny areas, but it is a great tool for cleaning up the woodlands, as well. Although it may take years for the wood to compost down, these piles eventually will produce very useful, fungally dominated compost. Of course, you can run the woody debris through a chipper, which increases the surface area of the debris and substantially speeds decomposition.

Woody compost does wonders for forest medicinals, and is also a great choice for protecting your perennials through the winter. Woody compost provides frost protection, as well as moisture retention, without overstimulating. I'll never forget watching my friend, Jeremy, turn over a large woody pile in order to rob the layer of compost that had accumulated underneath. He didn't wait for the whole thing to compost down, just went at it with a long bar, ant-like, until the entire pile rolled over and he could scrape up the goodies that had accrued underneath. He wanted to make some potting soil for growing false unicorn (*Chamaelirium luteum*), and nothing else would do.

Soft debris is composed of grass clippings, weeds from the field, kitchen garbage, tree leaves raked from the yard or the woodlot, dead vines pulled down from a trellis—any readily decomposable material that occurs on the farm. The soft debris pile can be layered and turned in the traditional manner, thereby creating organic compost within a few months. This is the standard method of composting, where carbon-rich ingredients (e.g. hay, straw, or tree leaves) are layered with nitrogen-rich ingredients (e.g. kitchen garbage, green grass clippings, or animal manures). The pile heats up, you turn the pile manually, it heats up again, you turn it again, and eventually you get black humus that smells like rich soil (not garbage).

Another method of working with soft ingredients is to simply pile them up as they become available, grass clippings one day, pigweed pulled out of the corn patch the next day, the marc (leftover press cake) from pressing goldenseal tincture the following day, and so on. The ingredients can be piled higher and higher and not turned. This is lazy-man's composting, and I'm mentioning it here because, although aerobic composting with turning is ideal, there is really nothing wrong with piling up soft debris and letting it work at its own speed. This method is problematical only if the pile turns anaerobic, which means that the ingredients are too nitrogen-rich and are not getting enough oxygen. Avoid this situation by covering kitchen waste or raw manure inputs with copious quantities of dry, carbon-rich ingredients. Don't worry, the pile will eventually decompose and produce very serviceable organic compost, slowly, usually within a year or two.

I remember once making a pile of this sort, adding all kinds of coarse ingredients as I cleaned up the gardens around the seed house, piling up lots and lots of brown, overgrown stem material from the previous year. The pile got taller than I was, so that I had to toss the materials up on top, and it stayed that way through the spring and into the summer. It wasn't heating up, it wasn't cooking down, and I wasn't worrying about it.

Meanwhile, the rains of early summer were coming down and the grass was getting out of hand. We had to mow it soon, or we wouldn't be able to mow it at all! I finally convinced a neighborhood lad to help me out. He came over on a Saturday, wrapped his shirt around his head like a turban, plugged himself into an iPod, and started to mow. He would mow for a couple of minutes, then the mower would bog down, and he'd empty the bag onto the perimeter of the soft debris pile. Then he'd mow some more.

Eventually, he did get the job done, and my whole pile was thickly heaped over with grass clippings. We had a good rain that night, and about ten o'clock the next morning, I noticed a thin waft of steam rising from the pile. The next day, the pile was shouldering down and caving in on itself. I stuck my bare hand in. "Ouch," I said, pulling my steaming hand back out again. "That's *hot*!" The pile had reached critical mass—the nitrogen-rich grass clippings having provoked a complete melt-down.

By midsummer, I was using compost from that (unturned) pile in our potting soil for the nursery and also as a side-dressing around plants in the field, to give them a boost. It was really good stuff. My peppers were fantastic that year. However, I must have thrown a lot of jimson weed seed capsules into the compost pile somewhere along the line, because everywhere we put the compost, jimson weed sprouted adventitiously, and it all had to be weeded out by hand. Probably, gardeners like me who utilize "labor-saving" methods end up putting in the labor sooner or later, anyway.

Hot-composted, vegetarian. Layer carbon rich ingredients (e.g. straw, autumn leaves) with nitrogen-rich ingredients (ex. green lawn clippings, fresh comfrey leaves, or kitchen garbage). Do this during the warm months of the year, and make sure to employ sufficient volume of ingredients in order to reach critical mass. First lay down a thick layer of fluffed out straw (about 1 foot tall or so), then cover with at least 4 inches of nitrogen-rich ingredients, then put another layer of straw on top of that, then add more nitrogen-rich ingredients. Finish off with straw mounded over the top. This helps prohibit flies. A minimum-sized pile would utilize 3 bales of straw and sufficient grass clippings and kitchen garbage to create the necessary layers.

After piling, water down or wait for a good rain. Piles such as this will heat up smoking hot—a thermometer put into the center will show a temperature of 160° F or more. After a few days the volume of the pile will be somewhat reduced, and so it will be easier to turn, which of course is what you ought to do at this stage. Use a pitchfork (or the front loader on a tractor) and toss the top of the pile off to the side, then systematically toss the remainder of the pile on top of the top, so to speak. The layers will thus be reversed and the whole will be somewhat mixed.

Water sparingly, and let it compost again. This will take a few days during the summer and a few weeks during cooler weather. Turn the pile again. Once the compost no longer heats up after turning, it is finished, and you can use it. If heavy rains occur at any time during this process, it is a good idea to tarp the pile, as too much moisture will prevent the pile from heating up.

Hot-composted manure. Start the pile with a 1-foot thick layer of straw, then apply at least 4 inches of manure, then apply more straw, then more manure, then more straw. Cornstalks, leaves, or dried grasses may certainly be substituted for the straw. Allow the pile to heat up, and then turn it. After the pile has been turned and heated 3 times, the volume will be vastly reduced, and the compost will be ready to use. Give it the nose test—if it's finished, it will smell like good earth. If it smells like poop, then turn it again!

Aged manure. Manures cannot be used green—they must first be hot-composted or they may be aged by piling and leaching in the sun and rain for at least 6 months before use. Piled manures will have better texture and uniformity if they are turned once or twice during the aging process, or you can aerate the pile by running your rototiller through it. Whether hot-composted or piled, in time, the content of undigested carbon will be reduced and the content of worm castings will be increased (always a good trade).

Chicken manure is very high in nitrogen, but can be overly moist when it emerges from the bird, so it tends to be quite messy and stinky to work with. Chicken manure will certainly produce great compost if you can devise a method to break it up sufficiently, then layer it with carbon and compost in the usual manner. Uncomposted, broken up, dried chicken

manure is a great starter for cover crops, as it is easy to spread and a little bit goes a long way. Prepare a fine seedbed, scatter the manure, till it in, then spread the seed, rake it in, and tamp well. In this way, you can assure coverage of even the most depleted soils.

When planting corn, make furrows 6 inches deep and sprinkle in a little chicken manure. Cover the manure with 1 inch of soil, drop in the corn seeds, then cover with soil, tamp, and water. Try to do this at a time when there is much sunshine. The corn will thrive on the chicken manure, and the weeds will not be able to reach it—you've placed it right under the corn, where it will do the most good!

If there is a concern that the manure may contain many noxious weed seeds, then use it during transplant. Dig a hole, carefully introduce half a shovelful of compost, place the plant in the hole, then fill in with dirt around the roots of the plant, making sure to bury the compost well below the surface of the soil. Most weed seeds are light-dependent germinators, and they won't germinate if they have to make their way through several inches of overburden, so this method makes use of the power of compost while minimizing the introduction of unwanted weed species.

Horse manure is not as good as other manures, in my opinion. I find it obnoxiously stinky and the bedding mixed in with the manure tends to harbor nematodes (plant parasitic worms). Horse manure also contains a great many viable weed seeds, which can cause much work if they are spread back on your garden. Therefore, horse manure needs to be thoroughly hot-composted before use. Since horses are often fed on hay and bedded down on straw, it is often possible to find composted manure in the vicinity of the stalls, where it has been tossed out by the stable cleaners and has spontaneously composted.

Manure from other hoofed beasts, including llamas, sheep, and goats, is quite nice. My main experience is with the manure from my alpine goats. Since we feed the goats with weeds from the garden, it's really a tight little cycle right here on the land: weeds to goats to manure to compost to field to weeds to goats to manure to compost to field . . . I compost the contents of the stalls in a big pile outside the goat shed. The manure and urine-soaked bedding is mixed with the leftover hay from their feed, and it heats up quite efficiently. I usually turn it once and run the rototiller through it to finish it off. I find that this compost works well for high nitrogen crops, such as: artichokes, basil, gourds, squash, sunflowers, corn, beans, and peppers.

Rabbit manure is actually extraordinary. Those magnificent little balls have a very high nitrogen content, but even when used in the raw form, they do not readily burn the plants. Rabbit manure composts quickly, but requires a lot of aeration, as it can easily get too wet, cake, and go anaerobic. Composted rabbit manure is quickly assimilated into the soil and is particularly well-suited for growing cucumbers, peppers, and house plants.

Cow manure is the best all-around choice for the medicinal herb farm, due to its superior texture and mellow balance of nutrients. Cow manure as it comes out of the cow is already a composite of our two favorite compost-making elements—carbon and nitrogen. Grasses and grains are mixed, broken down, and mellowed by passing through the multichambered digestive tract of this placid ruminant. Washed cow manure is widely available from the big dairies, being the leftover product after fresh manure is washed out of the stalls, piled, and drained. Whenever possible, choose organically certified dairies as the source of your manure. Washed cow manure must still be aged or composted before use, but it breaks down quickly, and it is truly a preferred ingredient for medicinal herb growing, where good soil structure is more important than high nitrogen content.

CHAPTER 18 — POTTING SOILS

How to make potting soil. Potting soils are the essential substance used for filling flats, as well as for potting up greenhouse plants, indoor plants, planters, and for layering in the furrow or in the tortuga. Potting soils are best composed of a mix of several ingredients formulated to match the needs of the individual plant. Common vegetables, such as cucumbers, peppers, and tomatoes, will prosper in potting soils composed mainly, or even solely, of compost or composted manure. Medicinal herbs, (for the most part recently derived from their wild counterparts), prefer potting soils that more closely resemble soils as they are found in nature.

As discussed previously (in chapter 6), soils as they are found in nature are composed of a mixture of mineral soil and humus. In order to approximate the qualities of natural soil, good potting soil is also composed of an admixture of mineral ingredients and humus. This chapter discusses ways to make live potting soil that will help engender success in convincing wild plants to grow in pots and in the garden. The main ingredients used are: coarse, sharp sand (ideally delivered from a local quarry); white, horticultural pumice; coir (ground coconut husk); and compost or composted manure. Like decomposed rock in mineral soils, the sand and the pumice provide drainage and nutrients. Like humus in natural soils, the coir and the compost hold everything together.

Although all the ingredients are important, the quality of your potting soil is really determined by the quality of your compost—the better the compost, the better the potting soil. Finding the ideal mix for each type of medicinal herb is not only a good way to get it to grow well—it is often the only way to get it to grow at all!

Live soils. In nature, seeds germinate naturally in soils that are teeming with bacteria, are interlaced with fungal mycelia, and are aerated by worms, pill bugs, insects, and burrowing vertebrates. Bacteria and fungi interact with the embryonic root radicle, serving to increase the bioavailability of water, nutrients, and essential plant hormones (e.g. gibberellic acid) to the developing seedling.

Medicinal herb growers do well to make potting soil that contains living bacteria and fungi, in order to match the natural germination conditions normally encountered by plants in the wild. This advice is at odds with the common practice of sterilizing potting soil with heat or chemicals. This is done to reduce problems with damping-off disease and to kill the seeds of adventitious weeds. However, damping off disease is best avoided by making sure not to overwater the flats on cool days, and weeds are best controlled by pulling. Read on to discover the various tools, techniques, and substances that spell success in creating live potting soils.

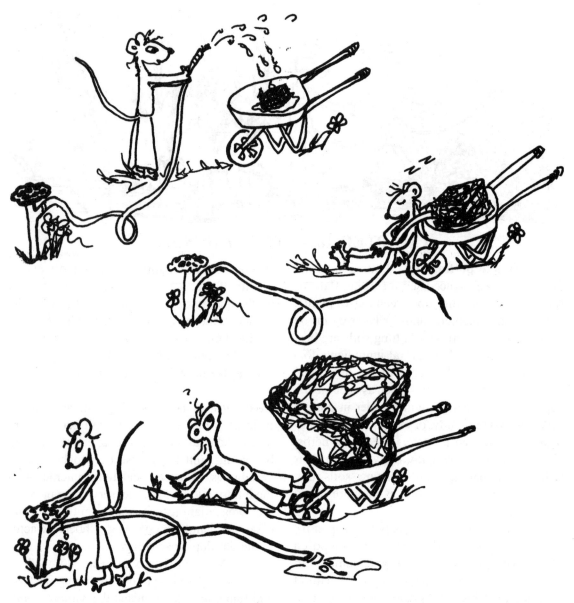

Coir is the aged, ground up pith of the coconut pericarp that provides an excellent base for good organic potting soil. For most applications, coir works better than peat moss. Coir is pH neutral and more ecologically appropriate. Most horticultural-grade coir comes in dried, compressed bricks. These can be reconstituted into a fine, reddish, good-smelling, crumbly humus by soaking them in water, usually using a half-barrel or a watertight wheelbarrow. It takes about 5 gallons of water to hydrate an 11 lb. block of dried, compressed coir. Pour the water over the block of coir and let it sit in the puddle (see illustration). Good quality coir will swiftly absorb the water and may be crumbled apart by hand and made ready to use within an hour or so of adding the water. The one drawback of coir is that it has a high potassium content, so a small amount of ground limestone or gypsum ($1/4$ cup per 11 lb. block) is best mixed into the moist coir before use. The rock powder binds the potassium to nullify any deleterious effects.

Mix your own. Many growers purchase bagged or bulk potting soil, which may or may not be a good choice. Making your own assures good quality, is a great deal less expensive, and allows you to customize according to the needs of the plants at hand.

The basic procedure is to first choose an open, airy place that is level and well-drained. Second, to gather materials in workable piles around you. Third, to measure out these materials in the correct proportions. A balance between water-retentive and fast-draining materials gives good results in most cases. The fourth thing is a bit obvious—one must contrive somehow to evenly mix these materials together in order to make use of them as potting soil. In this lies the . . . work.

On a very small scale, you can keep your ingredients in 5-gallon buckets and mix on any level surface, like a table, cement slab, or level, dry, grassless ground. The ingredients are doled out, the micronutrients are sprinkled on, and everything is kneaded together by hand like bread until completely homogenous.

For somewhat larger applications, it is best to incorporate all ingredients with a shovel in a wheelbarrow. In this, you might feel like a miniature kid trying to mix a giant bowl of your breakfast cereal with an outsize spoon, assisted only by a doubtful dose of watery milk, mixing, there, somewhere in the suburbs.

Following, find recipes for making increasingly larger batches of potting soil, starting with small mixing and ending in the mixing trench. In these recipes, I had the assistance of my friend, Erich, who took my materials and ran with them, and who has a mystical touch with plants and soil.

Potting soil mixture for houseplants: The standard of measure is the "gallon pot," something almost everybody has kicking around in a corner somewhere. One gallon is also the breakout volume of the smallest commercially available block of coir, which makes this recipe convenient for apartment dwellers and hobbyists.

1 gallon of hydrated coir
1 gallon of compost or composted manure
2 Tbsp. micronutrient mix (see below)
$1/2$ gallon coarse, sharp sand
1 gallon pumice

Using your hands or a hand trowel, mix all ingredients together very thoroughly.

Micronutrient mix:
1 cup kelp powder
$1/2$ cup colloidal rock phosphate
$1/2$ cup ground oyster shell
$1/2$ cup ground limestone

Taking precautions against inhaling the dust, pour all ingredients into a small bucket or bowl and mix thoroughly with a spoon.

Inoculants. Plants derive broad benefit from inoculation with native soils from the garden, fields, or woods. Adding a scant handful of such soils introduces fungal and bacterial microorganisms that act to balance the soil, and also a few weed seeds for entertainment. Forest plants, such as violets, will benefit when a bit of lively forest soil is added in to the mix. Vegetables like very rich compost, which serves to inoculate them. Cacti germinate and grow much better when soil taken from around other established cacti is introduced into the growing medium.

Standard, fast-draining potting soil by the wheelbarrowful:

8 shovelfuls of hydrated coir
8 shovelfuls of compost or composted manure
1 cup dried kelp
$1/2$ cup colloidal rock phosphate
$1/2$ cup ground oyster shell
$1/2$ cup ground limestone
2 shovelfuls of coarse, sharp sand
8 shovelfuls of horticultural-grade pumice

Mix with a shovel or a hoe right in the wheelbarrow, use a (clean) cement mixer, or throw the ingredients by the shovelful up on top of a table screen ($1/2$-inch mesh) and screen everything through by hand into a pile or a wheelbarrow below.

To build a table screen, use a 3 x 4 foot piece of $1/2$-inch mesh hardware cloth tacked to a 2 x 6 frame held up by four 3-foot legs. It is best to screen the ingredients through twice to thoroughly mix them. Running potting soil through a screen really fluffs it up and gives you the chance to remove objects, such as: oversize rocks, corncobs, chunks of bark, and unmentionables from the potting soil.

Standard, fluffy, moisture-retentive soil by the wheelbarrowful:

12 shovelfuls of hydrated coir
8 shovelfuls of compost or composted manure
1 cup dried kelp
$1/2$ cup colloidal rock phosphate
$1/2$ cup ground oyster shell
$1/2$ cup ground limestone
2 shovelfuls of coarse, sharp sand
3 shovelfuls of horticultural-grade pumice

Alternative ingredients. If you cannot locate coir, then use peat. If you do not have compost, then you can use aged animal manure. Another good substitute for compost is worm castings, which can be produced on-site or purchased by the bag. Use only $1/3$ as much worm castings as compost—they make a very rich blend. If you do not have pumice, you can use perlite. If you can't find rock phosphate, you can substitute wood ash.

These recipes are good all-around organic mixes for growing many medicinal annuals, perennials, vines, bushes, and trees, especially those that do well in bacterially dominated systems (i.e. regular garden soil). The fast-draining mix is best for trees and plants with taproots that like plenty of drainage (e.g. ginkgo or *Echinacea angustifolia*). The moisture-retentive mix is better for plants that have spreading root systems and don't like drying out (e.g. boneset or *Echinacea purpurea*).

For forest plants that love carbon-rich, fungally dominated soils, such as goldenseal, spice bush, and black cohosh. Double the coir; halve the compost, sand, and pumice; use wood ashes instead of rock phosphate; and add a half shovelful of forest soil as an inoculant.

For plants that do best in areas of poor drainage, such as cardinal flower (*Lobelia cardinalis*), boneset, and gravel root. Double the coir; halve the sand, limestone, and rock phosphate; double the kelp; and exclude the pumice.

For plants that love acid-loam soils found at high elevation, or for plants that generally associate with coniferous forests, such as: *Arnica montana*, Chinese coptis, yellow gentian, or yarrow. Use peat moss instead of coir; exclude the sand, phosphate, and lime; halve the pumice; add $1/2$ shovelful of high elevation acid-loam soil as an inoculant.

For plants that love desert conditions, such as: licorice (*Glycyrrhiza glabra*), mandrake (*Mandragora officinalis*), Mormon tea (*Ephedra nevadensis*), and white sage. Use coir instead of peat moss; halve the compost; double the sand and the limestone; inoculate with $1/2$ shovelful of sand from the desert.

For cacti. Halve the coir and the compost; double the sand, limestone, and pumice; add soil from around existing cacti as an inoculant. Cactus mixes must contain at least 50% fast-draining ingredients, such as pumice or coarse, sharp sand—preferably both.

For crossover herbs/vegetables, such as: artichokes, asparagus, basils, cucumbers, and peppers, use a compost-dominated potting soil. Halve the coir and the pumice; double the compost. The best inoculant for vegetables is compost, whether derived from animal manure or vegetarian. Heavy feeders, such as tomatoes and peppers, may prefer to grow in pure compost, and may benefit greatly from potting up in successively larger containers. They are greedy little pigs that need a fat teat.

The mixing trench. For larger greenhouses, the table screen soon becomes inadequate for mixing the volume of potting soil that is truly needed. As my friend, Dale, in Georgia once told me "A man would have to have a weak mind and a strong back to mix up all that stuff by hand!" I admit that here at our nursery we used to fit that description nicely until we started using a cement mixer to mix our potting soil. The cement mixer proved to be too small and too slow for our purposes, so we upgraded to "the mixing trench." This method may prove very helpful to anyone who owns a rototiller and uses a great deal of potting soil. Locate the mixing trench near the greenhouse. Pile ingredients nearby. Sand, pumice, and coir are most economically purchased by the truckload, and it will save lots of human energy to locate the potting soil manufacturing area in a place where it can easily be accessed by dump trucks.

The mixing trench itself is composed of 2 timbers (4 x 6's or bigger), about 8 feet long, placed parallel to each other on level ground and spaced about 2 feet apart, wider or narrower depending on the bite of your tiller. Basically, these are bumpers. You want to leave about 3 inches on each side for slop factor, so for a tiller with a 20-inch tilling width, you would set the timbers 26 inches apart. The timber ought to be laid on edge to give maximum curb height. Drill a series of $3/4$-inch holes through the timber and then pin it to the ground with rebar or steel construction stakes.

Use only untreated timbers. Osage orange, black locust, cedar, or other rot-resistant woods, if available, are a great choice.

Instead of using the timbers, you may choose to create the same effect by laying cement blocks. Sometimes these are more readily available than wood. Lay the blocks in 2 short walls, 2 high, on level ground. You can lay them dry without cement, then pin them in place with pieces of steel t-posts or steel construction stakes driven into the holes in the blocks and down into the dirt. Then, fill the wall tightly with gravel, clay, sand, or pumice thereby locking the blocks securely in place. You could lay the block with cement, but that would make it very difficult if you ever want to rearrange the furniture.

The basic idea is to layer the soil-making ingredients between the two bumpers (the timbers or the cement block walls) and then run the rototiller through to mix them up. As the tiller passes through the trench, the potting soil will try to escape, but it will fall back around the tines of the tiller when it comes in contact with the bumpers. It cannot escape. It must be mixed. This truly is an efficient way to mix potting soil by using machinery at hand, but *use caution.* Use low gear, please, and keep hands and feet away from the whirring tines.

Standard, fast-draining potting soil by the trenchful:

2 wheelbarrowfuls hydrated coir
2 wheelbarrowfuls compost/composted manure
2 cups kelp
1 cup colloidal rock phosphate
1 cup ground oyster shell
1 cup ground limestone
1 wheelbarrowful coarse, sharp sand
2 wheelbarrowfuls horticultural-grade pumice

Layer the ingredients in the trench. Start by spreading out the hydrated coir. (A wheelbarrow contains about 30 shovelfuls, so that's 60 shovelfuls). It ought to be moist through and fairly well broken-up, but it doesn't have to be completely fluffed (as it would be if you rubbed it through a table screen), because now the rototiller will finish it off.

Then layer the finished compost on top of the coir and spread out evenly, using a shovel or your feet. Mix the kelp, rock phosphate, oyster shell, and limestone together and sprinkle over the compost. Then spread the sand on top of that. Top off the pile with the pumice. Then run the rear-tine rototiller through the trench, allowing the tines to go down to the bottom of the trench and really mix things up. It usually takes 4 or 5 passes to thoroughly mix all ingredients. It's not difficult tilling, and you can tell when the potting soil is completely homogenous.

Fills roughly 18 flats that are 5 inches deep and 16 inches square.

Standard, fluffy, moisture-retentive soil by the trenchful:

3 wheelbarrowfuls hydrated coir
2 wheelbarrowfuls compost/composted manure
2 cups kelp
1 cup colloidal rock phosphate
1 cup ground oyster shell
1 cup ground limestone
1 wheelbarrowful coarse, sharp sand
2/3 wheelbarrowful horticultural-grade pumice

Fills roughly 18 flats that are 5 inches deep and 16 inches square.

CHAPTER 19 — PLANTING SEEDS

Direct-seeding. Dropping fertile seeds directly into the soil of garden or field is one of the best inroads to practicing natural gardening techniques. It is the method that tends to produce the strongest, happiest plants. If one has sufficient feel for working within the seasonal windows of opportunity, then there is a good chance of establishing a robust stand in this manner. Of course, due to weed pressure, this method may not be effective for growing slow-germinating seeds. Direct-seeding in the field is at its best when working with large seeds that germinate within 3 weeks of planting, but with skill, it is possible to work with the majority of seeds in this manner. The advantage of direct-seeding is that the plants, and most especially the roots of the plants, grow in a natural and uninterrupted manner (no transplanting) and there is a great saving of human and earth resources—less labor, no plastic.

Direct-seeding on a small scale may be accomplished by hand-forking the soil to prepare a fine seedbed. When gardening by hand, beds are usually made 4-feet wide (so that you can reach into the middle from either side and weed the whole bed) with 2 to 4 rows of plants in each bed, depending on the size of the plants. When using a rototiller, I like to direct-seed smaller plants (e.g. calendula) in 2-foot wide swaths, which are then thinned out into triangles once the seedlings establish themselves, with the plants finally spaced 1 foot apart. I like to direct-seed larger plants (e.g. *Echinacea purpurea*) in narrow rows, thinning the plants to 2 feet apart in the row. The rows can be maintained by tilling up the sides, so the practical distance between the rows is a little wider than the bite of the rototiller.

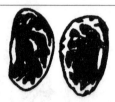

On larger farms, it is probably best to maintain such rows with a tractor fitted out with a cultivator. Many farmers prepare a slightly raised 4-foot wide bed and make 3 rows in the bed. Regardless of how one arranges things, cultivating occasionally between the rows and between the plants in the rows controls weeds, aerates the roots, and gives the developing plants space to grow.

The ideal window of opportunity for preparing the seedbed is when the spring rains abate and the ground dries sufficiently. Tilling when the ground is too wet will ruin the structure of the soil for the season. I wait until the ground is dry enough so that tillage creates a fluffy soil surface, tilling especially deeply where I plan to plant my seeds. If rain intercedes, then I must wait again until the ground dries sufficiently to produce the right soil.

A good rule of green thumb for this is to pick up a handful of dirt, squeeze it tightly, and then attempt to break the clod apart by poking it with a finger. If it maintains its cloddy structure, then do not till. If the clod breaks apart into relatively fine and fluffy particles, then it's time to get to work. Another method for checking soil moisture is to watch the wheels of the rototiller. If they pick up mud, then it is probably too wet to till. If they stay clean, then you are good to go.

I use a powerful, rear-tine rototiller. I sometimes check the biodynamic calendar and, in general, plan to use my machines during the dark of the moon, or in conjunction with the planets Mercury and Mars. Tilling is hard work, and if the planets can help deter the weeds, then I say, let them. If there are a large number of weed seeds from light-dependent germinators already in the soil, then tilling during the brightest part of the day will probably activate many of them. In this case, it's a good idea to till in the late afternoon and evening.

The job of working the cover crop into the soil often requires several sessions of tilling, starting with a coarse twice-over, then a few days wait, followed by several more passes. This produces a fine seedbed, unencumbered by grass roots or rotting herbage. I wait long enough between these sessions of tilling for weeds to come up, which substantially reduces the weed seed bank in the soil. I till again. These are weeds that I will not have to hoe or pull by hand later. The early spring tilling session is also a good time to broadcast and till in rock powders, such as colloidal phosphate and lime, as well as compost, according to the needs of the soil and according to the feeding habits of the plants that will soon grow there.

Given the variations in size of medicinal herb seeds, I find it impractical to use machinery or other contrivances for planting seed, preferring instead to plant the seed by hand. It's such a holy act, putting seed to soil, and it connects us with the positive earth-bound efforts of our entire lineage of ancestors. I like to feel the seed and think about how much all beings will benefit. Besides, it took so much work to get to this point, that one might as well savor the act. This is what I call *fun*. Small seeds are mixed with sand prior to planting, then strewn directly on the slightly rough surface and pressed in hard. Larger seeds usually require a shallow furrow, which can be made quite easily with a hoe or the tip of a spade.

If one is using a furrow, it makes sense to band the compost directly under the crop instead of broadcasting it. This will keep the fertilizer right where the crop plants need it, and it will fertilize the seeds you're planting— not the weed seeds. Mix the compost in with the soil within the furrow, fill your hand with seeds, and let them dribble into the row.

If the soil is loaded with weed seeds, this can really get in the way of direct-seeding medicinal herbs. In this case, you can make a furrow 4 inches deep and 6 inches wide, and fill it with weed-seed-free potting soil. Plant your medicinal herb seeds in the potting soil. In this way, you will be able to recognize the crop seeds when they germinate, instead of losing them amongst the rampant weeds.

When direct-seeding, it is better to plant more seeds than you think necessary, because there is always some natural attrition and it is not too hard to go back later and thin to the desired spacing. Still, do not grossly overplant the seeds, or the seedlings will be small, difficult to thin, and in competition with each other. Following, find some suggestions on how many seeds to plant in order to produce sufficient seedlings, but not too many.

For large seed of dependable germination (such as artichoke), a good rule of green thumb is to plant 3 times (not 30 times) more seed than the desired number of plants you want to end up with. Plant thinly on the first pass, to make sure you have enough seed to get to the end of the row, then if you have some seed left, go over it again and drop more seeds in the sparse spots.

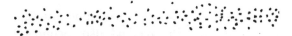

For small seed, such as *Artemisia annua*, planting 30 times more seed than the desired number of eventual plants is not excessive. This is because, in field conditions, small seed tends to germinate at a far lower rate than if you were to plant it in the controlled conditions of the greenhouse.

The desired finished spacing of the plants depends on many factors. Root form is a major consideration. *Echinacea purpurea,* with its spreading root system, must be planted at least 12 inches apart, while *Echinacea angustifolia,* with its taprooted habit, may be planted as closely as 4 inches apart. Eventual size of the plant is a critical factor—you want to give them elbowroom, but maximize yield. Water availability and method of watering is another important factor here. If dryland farming, space the plants further apart, so they don't compete for limited water resources. If relying on drip lines, then space the plants with drip compatibility in mind.

Another good direct-seeding technique is to scatter the seed in a bed or a wide, running swath, instead of restricting the planting to a narrow furrow. Prepare the seedbed to the desired width and length. Scatter the seed by hand over the surface, rake it in, and tamp. Some of the seeds will end up on the surface, but if you tamp well, even this seed will germinate. This method produces a natural distribution of seedlings that may be thinned and triangulated within the swath. An advantage of this technique is that it instills better resistance to pests (the gopher can't eat all the

marshmallow by earth-swimming straight down the row). This method also encourages better cross-pollination, and therefore increased seed vigor and better overall yield, as more of the field is dedicated to the plants.

However, plants situated in a wide swath will probably require more labor to cultivate and weed than if they were arranged in single rows. In any case, you can maintain the planting by tilling down the sides of the swath, thereby creating human access and keeping at least some of the weeds easily in check. Cultivate the soil as closely to the crop plants as you can without tilling them under or causing damage to their roots. Plants love to be cultivated, as soil structure is optimized for aeration and water-holding capacity, while nutrients are stirred up and made soluble for ready assimilation.

Ultimately, you must hand-release each plant by hoeing or hand-cultivating weeds that were missed by the tiller. Time for rubber fingers. Swirl the soil around the plant with a loose, loving caress. Cultivate shallowly and often, as weeds will be much harder to get rid of if you let them get established. If the weeds get the better of you, then roll up your sleeves and get ready for a lot of work—you must now pull them by hand.

mental chatter with the soothing voice of nature. This is your moment in the sun, and life in the garden is good.

Appreciate it now. Don't overexert. Soak up the sun and drink water. In this way, you aren't really much different from a plant. When organisms share similar ways of life, communication is only natural. Talk to your plants. Exhort them to do their best. Think of those who will eat the plants or use the medicine made from their roots, leaves, and flowers. Think of those who will plant the seeds again. Pray earnestly that your efforts will benefit all beings.

Feel free to deconstruct your own mental/spiritual/physical blockages while pulling weeds. Chant, sing, or be quiet and listen to the plants, birds, insects, and frogs. Replace

114

rows in the same flat with good success. In another flat, you might plant 5 different rows of small, surface-sown seeds by roughing up the surface, sprinkling on the seed, then securely tamping. In most cases, the best practice is to cover the seeds with $1/8$ inch of soil and tamp well.

Use a plant tag to label each type of seed with common and Latin name and the planting date. Also, enter the lot number of the seed if this is available. Gently water the flats. Keep them in the appropriate environment for the kinds of seeds that are in them, such as the greenhouse, the shadehouse, or in a sheltered spot outdoors in the open garden or the woods.

Sowing seeds in flats. Deep flats will measure approximately 16 inches square and between 2 and 5 inches deep. Any larger than this and, for most people, they become too heavy to lift. Heavy-duty plastic flats that drain nicely are commercially available or you can build your own by nailing together cedar boards. If you decide to build your own flats, make sure to space the bottom boards 1 inch apart to encourage drainage. The deeper the flat, to a certain extent, the moister and cooler will be the growing medium. Therefore, it is often wise to plant tropical and warm-weather vegetable seeds in shallower medium (2 to 3 inches deep) where they will stay warmer, and to plant temperate and long-germinating seeds in deeper medium (4 to 6 inches deep) where they will stay cooler and have plenty of root room once they germinate and grow.

Fill the flat with fast-draining potting soil and tamp. Now make up to 5 small, evenly-spaced furrows across the surface. Sprinkle in small seeds, watching the surface of the flat carefully while doing so, in order to gain a feel for how the seed is laying down, where it is going, and how many are being planted. Larger seeds may be planted individually.

Seeds requiring the same kinds of germination conditions are planted together in a flat. For instance, large seeds that require cold-conditioning may be planted in different

Dormancy and cold-conditioning. Wild seeds, upon release from the mother plant, are often loaded with germination-inhibiting compounds, such as: abscisic acid, dormin, waxes, and various essential oils. There is survival advantage to delayed germination—it is nature's way of making sure that some of the seeds, at least, will germinate during a time when they can survive to grow into mature plants. Germination-inhibiting chemicals do have a half-life, so they will lose their potency with time, and eventually the reproductive urge of the seeds will be likely to overpower the prohibitive effect of inhibitors. Such chemicals can also be leached from the seeds by watering and especially by the influence of rain and snow.

115

The expansion and contraction of the seeds as temperatures oscillate from cold to warm, night to day, and season to season, stimulates seed germination. Seeds that fail to respond to standard greenhouse technique will often germinate if moved into outdoor conditions. For instance, seeds of common weeds like dandelion and plantain can be surprisingly resistant to germination in the greenhouse, but may germinate readily when exposed to outdoor conditions.

Impermeable seed coat. Seeds with water-impermeable seed coats must have their seed coat scarified (i.e. nicked, pierced, or rubbed through) or they will not imbibe water. If they do not imbibe water, they cannot germinate. A good example of this is lotus (*Nelumbo nucifera*). The seed is encased in an extremely hard shell and remains viable for centuries. The seed must be scarified before germination is possible. This particular species is so hard that nicking with a knife is not really effective—it works better to rub the seeds individually on sandpaper until the white endosperm is just barely exposed. The seed is then dropped in water, which it absorbs, and the hard seed coat is softened by enzymatic activity, making it possible for the embryonic leaves and elongating radicle to split the seed coat asunder.

Scarify small seeds, such as astragalus and wild indigo, by rubbing them around on a piece of medium grit sandpaper. Larger seeds, such as licorice and hibiscus, may be scarified by grasping each seed individually and rubbing on sandpaper or nicking with a sharp blade until the white endosperm is exposed in one small spot. Do not scarify directly on the hilum (i.e. the scar of attachment.)

To test whether a seed needs scarification or not, drop it in water overnight. If it swells up, then it is imbibing water and probably does not need scarification. If it stays hard and does not swell, then it needs to be scarified. Scarify, soak overnight, and plant the swollen seeds the next day.

Soaking is when seeds are dropped in water and left to imbibe water overnight or, in some cases, for an extended period of time. I find that this works well with the large seeds of many tropical plants, water plants, as well as certain leguminous seeds that have tough seed coats. However, the vast majority of seeds are designed by nature to easily imbibe water after planting. Soaking seeds of this sort can make them susceptible to rot after planting. It is not a good idea to soak small seeds, as they do not require this treatment, and it makes them difficult to plant, because they glom together and adhere to your fingers.

Scarification with hot water. Certain leguminous tree seeds (for example, carob) germinate best when scarified, then dropped into very hot water, and left overnight and planted in the morning. Boil the water, remove it from the stove, and pour it into a cup with the scarified seeds inside. When this process works well, the response is obvious, as the seeds will swell substantially by morning. Once planted, germination is usually quite fast. Bottom heat can be helpful with seeds of this sort.

Light-dependent germinators are those seeds that require exposure to light before germination is possible. The chemical pathway is through the solar activation of the protein pigment phytochrome. Seeds exhibiting this adaptation are typically small, such as the seed of wormwood, Saint John's wort, and mullein. An example of light-dependent germination would be when a monocrop hayfield that has had no tillage for several years is tilled and suddenly gives birth to an entire crop of common mullein. Dormant seeds are awakened by sudden exposure to light.

In the greenhouse or in the outdoor nursery bed, light-dependent seeds are best surface-sown and pressed in firmly. In order to distribute the seeds more evenly, they may be mixed with sand prior to sowing in a row or broadcasting. I use at least twice the volume of sand as seeds, mixed together in a bowl or the bottom of a bucket. Sand deposited on the surface along with the seeds physically supports it in place, promotes drainage, discourages damping-off, and marks the planting.

Hard seed. Any given lot of wild plant seed will be likely to contain some hard seed, which is seed that although not dead resists imbibing water, resting inert even when planted in favorable circumstances. For instance, I usually expect a 30% initial germination of seed of wild Saint John's wort, with about 70% of hard seed that may germinate at a later time. The factors effecting germination of hard seed may be time, light dependency, oscillating temperatures, leaching of inhibitors, expansion and contraction in response to freezing temperatures, and/or the presence of gibberellic acid in the growing medium.

Gibberellic acid (GA3) is a hormonal stimulant to seed germination. GA3 is normally produced inside the seed coat when seeds imbibe water and enzymes begin to break down starches into sugar—plant energy. Some species are incapable of producing their own GA3 and must rely on exogenous GA3, which

is released when fungi break down in the soil. Good examples of this are bloodroot, datura, and pulsatilla, which are all stimulated by the presence of GA3. This is one of the reasons why we need to keep our potting soils alive, as sterilized potting soil will be unlikely to contain GA3.

Fire-dependent germination is a term given to seeds that germinate best after they are subjected to the influences of smoke and intense heat. This is a survival skill developed by pioneer species that typically emerge in the aftermath of fires, are stimulated by fire to germinate, and make use of the weed-free and ash-fertilized soils to grow quickly once germination does occur. The germination of white sage and bearsfoot (*Polymnia uvedalia*) is stimulated by fire.

To fire-treat seeds, first bury the seeds about $1/4$ inch deep in the flat (to protect them from incineration). Then build a flash fire on top of the planting. Use tinder-dry kindling (dry split wood or pinecones) and heap it about 6 inches deep, torch the fire and let it burn down, then water the flat through the cold ashes. Of course, reasonable precaution is advised when fire-treating seeds—don't use plastic, it will melt. Instead, use a ceramic pot or a wooden flat with soil heaped over the sides to protect the wood from burning.

My friend, Chauncey, was a buyer and seller of saw palmetto berries. His seed-drying sheds were conveniently located in saw palmetto country, the Pine Barrens near Waycross, Georgia. Fallen berries were swept from the sheds and discarded out back in a pile left open to the sun and rain. One would think that under these conditions, some of the berries would eventually germinate, but this never happened. Then, the pile accidentally caught fire, and was partially burned up before Chauncey heroically extinguished it with a garden hose. To Chauncey's surprise, in a few weeks, saw palmetto berries germinated rampantly along the edges of the burn. The saw-toothed seedlings emerged right through the ashes!

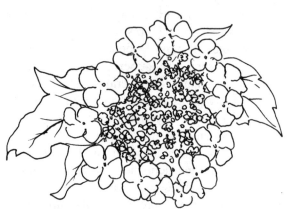

Heat-dependent germination. I use this term to describe seeds that must be subjected to consistently warm temperatures in order to germinate. Many tropical plants and desert plants do best if you "sow warm." The best example I can think of is yerba mansa (*Anemopsis californica*). This time the story starts with failure—I planted the seeds in a flat in the greenhouse and nothing came up. I waited and waited with no results. Often, it is the plants that send out vigorous runners or plants that are very easy to start from cuttings that make seeds that are hardest to germinate. Yerba mansa definitely falls into this class. In any case, I took the easy way out, reproducing my yerba mansa from runners.

Then a friend, who had set up a really nice propagation bench complete with hot water pipes running under the flats, planted some of the same yerba mansa seed that I'd had trouble with, but he attained excellent results after 3 months. Another grower gave me the news that her "manso" came up after an extended period of time in a flat left in the attic, where summer temperatures were soaring consistently past 100° F.

Later, I visited the Jemez hot springs outside Santa Fe in New Mexico. Lying there by the springs, observing the geothermal bubbling of mineral-rich waters over rocks colored in red and green slime, I realized that I was in the midst of a patch of dormant yerba mansa, the little coneheads dried out and camouflaged, rising in rust-red anonymity from the wintry leaf mass of the brown, desiccated leaves. Suddenly, it really made sense to me why they were growing there.

Multicycle germination simply means that after planting, the seeds are likely to require the passage of several seasons before germination is possible or before the germination of the planting is complete. I visualize the passing of seasons as temperature oscillation over time, which when graphed, produces the familiar wave pattern that one sees as the body print of the snake, or the form of waves at the beach, or the progress of a ray of light. It's this oscillation of seasonal temperature that softens the seed coat, stimulates the embryo, and eventually ignites the magic.

Slippery elm (*Ulmus rubra)* is a good example of a seed that responds to this seasonal wave pattern. When newly harvested and dried seed is planted, it may be expected to germinate at the rate of about 30% within 30 days. The remainder of the seeds will be multicycle germinators. I've seen them emerge vigorously the following spring and even the spring after that before the germination is complete.

Another seed that gives partial germination in the first year and more germination the following year is *Echinacea angustifolia.* Even milk thistle follows this pattern. Other examples of seeds that may require many seasons to germinate are cascara sagrada, cramp bark, elderberry, eleuthero, uva-ursi, manzanita, and Oregon grape. Germination time can sometimes be shortened by planting fresh seed, planting seeds newly washed out of the dried fruit, or by scarification.

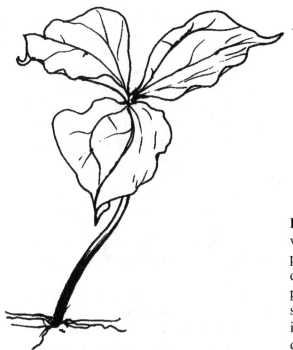

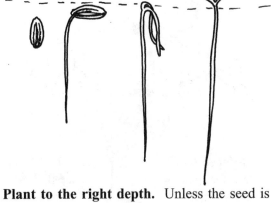

Plant to the right depth. Unless the seed is very large (bean-sized or greater) it is best to plant just under the surface of the soil. If you don't know how deeply small seed ought to be planted, then rough up the surface of the seedbed, strew the seed on the surface, work it in with the tips of your fingers, and tamp it down. This method gives a high rate of success.

Two-phase germination is where the seed makes a root in the first growing season, then produces aerial parts in the second growing season. Lily-of-the-valley and blue cohosh are 2-phase germinators. When the seed of these plants is spring-planted in the fresh, undried state, it will send out a root in the first growing season and make its first leaves in the spring of the second year. The survival advantage is that the plant is building up strength underground where there is little competition for resources. Then, when it is time to rise up and compete with other plants, the plant emerges from a more developed crown and quickly raises its little leaves and begins photosynthesis prior to the awakening of larger plants, which might otherwise grab the space as their own.

Ongoing germination is my term for seeds that give an original flush of germination and then give another flush of germination or sporadic germination for several additional weeks. Good examples of this would be cancer bush (*Sutherlandia frutescens*) and belladonna. It makes sense to retain the flats for long enough to allow for ongoing germination.

Tamp securely. Seed sown in loose soil will usually not germinate well, because it lacks a sense of place. When you tamp the soil, the seed is securely held in place with back-pressure from the surface, and has a chance to germinate and develop normally, without becoming dislodged, disoriented, and wasted. I cannot overemphasize the importance of tamping, a process demonstrated to me at an early date when I prepared a fluffy bed, planted it in German chamomile, took a patient breath as our large and flat-footed dog, Flow, walked over the newly planted bed, and marveled later when the chamomile emerged (only) in the dog tracks.

Leave the flats open to the air. Healthy air movement is essential to keeping your flats disease-free and will encourage seed germination. Water only when the surface of the flat begins to dry out. If this means watering twice a day, then so be it! Never, ever cover the moist flat of planted seeds with plastic—this will reduce your chances of success!

Watering the flats. Most seeds sprout best when the soil medium is very fast-draining, so that the water courses over the seed, the seed imbibes water, and then the medium drains before the next watering takes place. Gently water, then wait until the surface is nearly dry before again watering. These short cycles of watering followed by draining and resting create a kind of expansion-contraction phenomenon that effectively awakens seeds. There is time for the embryo to develop and then split the seed coat with its elongating radicle.

If the newly moistened seed goes bone-dry between waterings, this can be a problem, but an overly moist medium is more often the cause of failure. Cool and moist conditions encourage damping-off disease. This rots the roots when they emerge, or causes the seedlings to keel over and rot.

If the seeds need to be subjected to outdoor conditions in order to sprout, then the flats can be put on a bench in the open (like on a picnic table) or in the shadehouse. This allows you to make use of natural precipitation (snow and rain) to keep the seed moist, but if natural precipitation is not forthcoming, then the flats will need to be watered in order to keep the seed from drying out.

Take care when watering. If the seed begins to sprout and is then washed into a new position by overzealous watering, it may not have the energy resources to redirect its radicle again toward gravity. Seeds are best misted, not blasted. Imagine you are a gentle spring rain.

Nongermination. Remember that many medicinal herb species have been recently derived from the wild. Survival of the species depends on the seed's ability to wait until the right conditions are present before they "risk" sprouting. Be aware that many of these seeds can survive, quiescent but viable, for scores of years until the right conditions present themselves.

On one occasion, I decided that a (difficult to get) lot of kalmegh (*Andrographis paniculata*) was no longer viable. I'd planted it with no results, and I'm embarrassed to admit that my face wore a disgusted frown when finally I discarded the flats. However, another gardener had planted the same seed at the same time (early spring) and in the autumn gave me a call saying, "The kalmegh is full of pods—come over here if you want to pick some seed." I went over there and he was right—he had a couple of 300-foot rows of kalmegh from my seeds. The form of the plants was true to my memory of what the plant should look like, including the open, upright habit and the characteristically upright seedpods. You see, it was I who blamed the seed, but the seed was OK—the conditions I planted it in were simply not conducive!

120

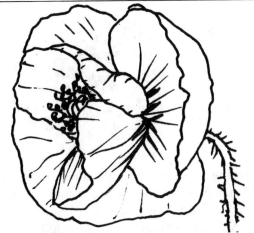

The conditions that lead to success in seed germination involve an understanding of the specific requirements of each species. The subject can become quite complex, and disparate theories about problematical germinators abound. For instance, many gardeners think that seed of angelica (*Angelica archangelica*) is very short-lived, but my experiments have shown a high rate of germination of seed that was stored in cold, dry conditions for the rather long period of 5 years. My original experiments with bloodroot (*Sanguinaria canadensis*) indicated that the seed had to be kept fresh (undried) and planted immediately in order to sprout, but another investigator showed that dry-stored seed germinated very well when grown in an environment that had a high level of GA3.

Many gardeners report low germination of passionflower (*Passiflora incarnata*) and widely disparate advice abounds. Some claim that the seed must be sown when very fresh, and even that it must never be removed from its jelly-like aril. Others swear that older, dry-stored seed gives results. Some recommend a period of cold, moist stratification, while others recommend soaking the seed for a week or two in very warm, bright conditions. My experiments have shown that the black seed is ripe seed, and gives higher germination than the white seed. In the fall, when newly harvested and dried, this black seed may be sown in a cold greenhouse, giving 90% germination within 3 months.

Giving advice about sowing seeds is a touchy subject, because the act of planting seeds is often charged with hope and fear. Separating fact from fiction is a lot like the act of separating seeds from chaff. Some methods yield clean seed, while others are wasteful. There are many variables involved, but they do fall into significant classes. Following, find a number of time-tested techniques that I find to be most effective.

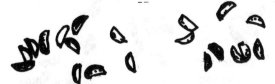

Sowing fresh (undried) seed as soon as ripe. Many seeds do not withstand dry storage and are quickly rendered useless if they dry out. Cascara sagrada, goldenseal, spice bush, and sweet wild grape are good examples. Seeds of this sort are best washed out of the fruit and planted immediately. Germination may occur quite rapidly, but it is more common to see spring germination of fall-planted seed.

Seeds in dried berries. Many seeds that expire very quickly in the clean, dried state are somehow preserved if stored intact in the dried fruit. I have noticed this phenomenon with goji (*Lycium barbarum*) and schisandra (*Shisandra chinensis*). Start by soaking the dried fruit overnight, then extract the seeds from the softened fruit, and sow. Germination of goji in nomal greenhouse conditions can be very rapid, while germination of schisandra requires cool, moist shade and multiple cycles.

Sowing newly harvested and dried seed soon after harvest. Many seeds, such as osha and dang-gui (*Angelica sinensis*), will withstand a short period of dry storage, but are relatively short-lived and are best sown soon after maturity. These seeds dry on the umbel and will give good results if sown in the fall, with germination in the spring. Seed stored for a full year and planted will give very low germination and produce seedlings of reduced vigor.

Some seeds germinate readily when newly harvested, but take on substantial dormancy once they are dry-stored for even a few weeks or months. A good example of this is dandelion, which germinates at a high rate if sown as a newly harvested and dried seed in the spring, but takes on strong dormancy and gives ongoing germination if stored for a month or longer prior to planting.

Sowing in spring. Spring is the busiest season for planting. Annuals must germinate in the spring or early summer in order to complete their life cycle by fall. *Artemisia annua*, chamomile, and mustard fall under this category. Biennials, such as: angelica, gobo burdock, wild lettuce, and woad, are also best started in the spring. Spring is a great time for planting most seeds, including many kinds of vegetables, herbaceous perennials, woody perennials, bushes, and trees.

Sowing in summer. Overwintering annuals germinate in the warm soils of summer or with the first fall rains, create low-lying rosettes that overwinter, then go quickly to flower and produce seeds the next summer. Anise, cumin, jewelweed, lobelia, maca, milk thistle, shepherd's purse, and poppy all fall under this category. Sometimes gardeners in severe winter areas attempt to plant overwintering annuals early in the spring, hoping to attain a harvest before winter sets in, but this is often unsuccessful or results in disappointing yields.

Sowing in summer to germinate in spring. Members of the crowfoot family, such as black cohosh, larkspur, and stavesacre require a cycle that progresses from warm summer temperatures, to cold winter temperatures, with germination as the ground warms up in the spring or early summer. Sowing the seed in the spring, or too late in the fall, will result in germination only after the requisite warm-cold-warm cycle has been satisfied.

Sowing in fall or early spring. Many seeds, whether common and easily germinated or rare and recalcitrant are of the sort that will withstand dry storage, but must be sown in the fall or very early spring for germination as the ground warms up in the spring. This mimics the natural cycle, where the dry seed is dispersed from the seedpod and falls to the earth, is softened and leached of germination inhibiting factors by rain and snow, and germinates when the ground warms in the spring. Good examples of this germination pattern are: alkanet (*Alkanna tinctoria*), false unicorn (*Chamaelirium luteum*), kiss-me-over-the-garden-gate, gentian, lomatium, osha, wasabi, and wild Job's tears.

Sowing according to the lunar cycle. The practice of astrology has much to offer in terms of helping us determine the best time to plant seeds. The biodynamic calendar is a helpful resource for anyone interested in timing the planting (and other farm activities such as cultivation, harvest, etc.) according to the moon, planets, and stars. A good rule of green thumb is to plant large, fast-germinating seeds a few days before the full moon, which gives the seeds time to imbibe water before germinating (usually) when the moon is full. Use this method when planting corn, beans, and squash, or fast-germinating medicinals, such as: artichoke, garden sage, basil, calendula, and borage. Slow-germinating flowers, such as echinacea, are best sown in the dark of the moon, with germination usually occurring during the next full moon, or an ensuing full moon.

Outdoor nursery bed technique. Probably the single most significant practice that I have learned to utilize for awakening recalcitrant germinators and rare and unusual medicinal plants (that are rare and unusual largely *because* they are slow and difficult germinators) is the outdoor nursery bed. Since slow germination times make direct-seeding in the field impractical for many species, we utilize an intermediary nursery bed to get the seedlings established prior to transplanting. Being in the open, nursery beds experience natural precipitation and daily and seasonal temperature fluctuation, producing germination of seeds that would probably not come up in a greenhouse, such as aconite, osha, and yellow gentian.

It's a great idea to maintain at least 2 outdoor nursery beds, 1 located in the full sun and 1 located in the shade. The beds can be made 4 feet wide, deeply dug, and amended with plenty of coarse, sharp sand for drainage.

The seedbed is prepared to a fine consistency and narrow furrows are scribed across its surface, spaced 6 inches apart. The seed is sprinkled in, covered, and securely tamped. The row is then marked with a stake and a tag in order to keep track of what has been planted, and when.

After the seeds germinate, the seedlings may be thinned to 1 or 2 inches apart. At first, the bed must be carefully weeded, but once the seedlings shoulder up, the rows can be mulched to prohibit weed re-emergence. The seedlings are grown until they obtain their second set of true leaves, then transplanted to the garden, field, or landscape.

Seedlings grown in this manner have naturally shaped root systems and leaves that are already inured to outdoor conditions, including the stress of sun and wind. Using this method, transplanting causes little shock, and the young plants tend to demonstrate excellent insect resistance, developing quickly into robust individuals.

Planting forest plants from seed. When herbs such as: ginseng, goldenseal, Jack-in-the-pulpit, and trillium make their seed, it is quite an event. The most convenient way to honor the occasion is to replant the seeds right away. Harvest the fresh fruits, remove the seeds from the fruit, and replant them before they dry out. This method gives excellent results.

If you have collected more than a small handful of fruits, then it is probably best to extract the seed by flotation. Smash the fruit in a small cloth bag, then empty the bag into a bucket and fill it with cold water. Give it a swirl. Immature seeds and flesh will suspend or float and can be carefully poured away. Good seed sinks to the bottom.

Plant the seeds singly in likely spots; strew them in the forest in good habitat, or better yet plant them in a nursery bed. The forest nursery bed can be prepared in essentially the same way as the bed made for planting roots, although it makes sense to break up the entire surface of the bed, not just the furrows. Remove rocks and roots and fluff up the soil. Prepare a fine seedbed, even it out, then make small furrows with your finger, 1 inch deep, in rows across the bed, 6 inches apart. Evenly distribute the fresh seeds in the furrow, 1 to 2 inches between the seeds, burying them just below the surface and tamping securely. Then cover the bed with a thin layer of fine leaf mulch. The new plants will emerge after 1 or 2 vernal (spring) cycles.

Seedlings require consistent availability of water, so if rains are not forthcoming, then you will have to water. The seedlings are allowed to grow at close spacing (not thinned). After developing for 1 or 2 years, the young rhizomes (pea-sized or larger) with their healthy head of rootlets can be dug up and replanted further apart. Again, such transplants are best performed in the autumn, after the aerial parts of the young plants die back.

Forest plants propagated from seed generally flower in the third year and ongoing. They are very disease-resistant and are really the most dependable and best producers. The rhizome may seem to increase slowly in the first and second year, but after transplant it will increase in size quite rapidly. My studies have shown that individual forest plants grown from seed give higher yields than clonal plants grown from cuttings.

WHY DIDN'T MY SEEDS COME UP?

A review of common mishaps. As long as your seeds are recent and have been properly cleaned and cared for, then they are very much alive. Even so, germination failures do occur. It is best to take this as a lesson, and to continually strive to improve your technique, in order to maximize your seed planting success. Following find a review of common seed planting errors and their remedies. It's all about providing the optimum conditions to invite in the miracle of life.

Failure to attend to the seasonal requirements of the plant. Much of the focus of this book has been to tune gardeners to using the seasonal cycles to best advantage. Sowing seeds at the wrong time of year, which can sometimes be equated to sowing seeds in soil that is not the ideal temperature, is a common cause of failure. For instance, seeds like borage and calendula do fine when planted in the warming soils of spring. However, seeds like blue flag, burning bush, and poppy are best planted in the cooling soils of fall. Before planting seeds, always attune yourself to the proper season for sowing that particular kind of seed. This practice will bring great success.

Not planting *enough* seeds. Nature instills seeds with germination-inhibiting compounds in order to encourage germination over several seasons. This is nature's method of hedging her bets on the survival of species through inclement conditions and disaster. Dormant seeds in the soil may take decades to germinate. Why, then, would gardeners think that medicinal herb seeds, largely unchanged from seeds in the natural state, should all germinate at once when they are planted by human hands in potting soil? They don't. That's why seed packets contain so many seeds. After planting, on the first flush, it is unusual to see 100% germination. If you were able to hold the flats for years, you would see more seeds germinating on an ongoing basis. But for the most part you can't do that, so instead—*plant the whole packet.* The practice of parting out one tiny seed per pot is bound to breed disappointment. Instead, sprinkle seeds generously, and if too many come up, then thin to the desired spacing.

Wrong potting soil. Planting seeds in peat pots which cannot drain properly, or planting in poor quality commercial potting soil that contains chemicals or fertilizers is the cause of many failures. Instead, mix your own potting soil that drains well, is alive like soils are in nature, and is customized for the plant.

Not enough potting soil. When gardeners come to us saying that they planted the seeds unsuccessfully in plug trays, small cells, or egg cartons, we encourage them to use bigger containers that don't dry out so quickly. Bigger containers also give the roots more room to develop normally. Fill a gallon pot with good quality potting soil, sprinkle the seeds on the surface, barely cover with more soil, tamp securely, and keep evenly moist and in the light until germination occurs.

Failure to adequately scarify the seed. Seeds with impermeable coats, such as licorice or marshmallow must be thoroughly scarified for best results. The seed is rubbed on medium grit sandpaper until the seedcoat is worn through in one small spot and the white endospem shows through. Then, the seed is planted. This method gives great results.

Planting too deeply. Seeds of common vegetables are for the most part large and can easily push their way up through $1/2$ to 1 inch of soil. Seeds of medicinal herbs are often quite small, and may not have the resources to push up through such a deep overburden of soil. Sow the seeds on the surface, barely cover with soil, and tamp securely. Most seeds do best when the flats are left in good light. Then, keep the soil evenly moist until the seeds come up. This method will give very good results for the majority of medicinal herb seeds. For light-dependent germinators (e.g. *Artemisia annua* or Saint John's wort), mix the very fine seed with sand, sprinkle the seed-sand mixture on the surface of the soil, do not cover with more soil, but tamp the seed securely into the surface of the soil and keep evenly moist until germination occurs.

Failure to tamp. Seeds must be tamped in securely in order to gain a sense of place. If they are not tamped, then they may tend to move around as they are being watered. If they send out their rootlet, and then are shifted, the rootlet must expend extra energy to reorient. With extremely robust species, this is usually not fatal. However, this simple oversight can easily exhaust a more delicate seed. Tamp the soil securely and reap the benefits!

Watering too much or too little. The best way to water the seeds is to give them a very gentle sprinkling, hydrating the surface, then allowing the soil to rest for a minute, and then sprinkling again. Do not allow the water to pool up above the seeds. This can be fatal. The soil should smell alive and wholesome, not dead or sour. Hydrate the soil very gently, allowing it to swell and expand around the seeds, holding them securely in place. Then, allow the soil surface to dry out slightly between waterings. Once the seedlings emerge, water every day, because seedlings are delicate and their little roots can't be allowed to dry out. Close attention to watering provides an essential element that supports the life of your plants.

Planting seeds on a windowsill. The old "pot on the windowsill" trick can work with certain species (such as the South African herb, hoodia) that perform well in a cool, low light situation, but in most cases it is a far cry from the results that can be obtained through direct seeding in a sunny garden or planting in pots using the standard greenhouse technique. Most plants require at least 6 hours of sunlight as a minimum light input for germination and normal growth. Accustom yourself to sowing the seeds in the garden, or start making plans for building a greenhouse!

Relying too heavily on grow lights. Starting seeds in flats under full-spectrum lights is a useful approach for starting many tropical species, and it can be a functional method for working with about 50% of temperate species. Grow lights are especially useful if you don't have a greenhouse, or if it's winter and you want to get a jump on the season. However, temperature oscillation is preferred for the germination of the remaining 50% of temperate species, so this method of starting seeds will not be appropriate 100% of the time! Furthermore, full spectrum lights simply are *not* the sun. Seedlings grown in these conditions will tend to grow very leggy as opposed to seedlings grown in natural light, which will be much stouter and more robust. Lights are sometimes helpful, but the sooner you get your plants into the sun, the happier they will be!

Putting seeds in and out of the freezer. When people hear that a seed requires cold-conditioning (stratification), they often think that putting the dried seeds into the freezer or the fridge is a suitable way to fulfill this requirement. However, putting dried seeds in the cold accomplishes nothing, because the seed must first imbibe water before it can make use of cold conditions. Furthermore, putting moist seeds in the freezer is often fatal to them, as it promotes formation of ice around the swollen embryo. For best results, if outdoor planting according to the seasons is not possible, place the seeds in moist medium (peat, coir, or sand) in a plastic bag and refrigerate for the requisite period of time, then plant in normal greenhouse conditions.

Planting between moist paper towels. The moist paper towel method is a common cause of failure. Paper towels contain bleach or other deleterious residues, they tend to keep the seeds too wet, there are no nutrients available, and normal development of the seed radicle and embryo are impossible. Instead, sow the seeds in good quality potting soil so they can expand and contract as they are watered and rested, and so they can send their radicle in the proper direction, and unfold their new leaves above the soil surface, into the sunlight.

Relying on bottom heat. Sometimes it works well to provide bottom heat. This is done by putting a small circulating oil heater under the table where the flats are held (take care not to burn down the house), or by using a commercially available heating pad that is designed for this purpose. It really depends on the specific seeds being planted as to whether this technique will or will not be helpful. For instance, the seeds of Chinese tea or chili peppers give fast and reliable germination in a bottom-heat situation, whereas astragalus, spikenard, or violet are likely to be killed by this treatment.

Prematurely discarding flats. Peas and beans come up right away in the spring garden, and many people assume that the same will be true of black elderberry and black cohosh. However, the germination cycle on these plants can easily take 6 months to 1 year. Learning to create the conditions for keeping seeded flats moist, shaded, and in oscillating temperatures (night to day, season to season) is critical. These conditions will lead to success in cultivating seeds that require a long germination period before any results can be expected.

Think positively. It is a well-documented fact that the good energy of the planter is a vital part of success in germinating seeds. While sowing, keep in mind that you really think this endeavor will be successful, and there is every reason to believe that the seeds will spring to life. Good practices for encouraging a positive approach may include humming or singing while you work. Some gardeners talk softly to the seeds while they sow. It may help to visualize the seed germinating, or envision the plant that will ensue. Dedicate the merit of sowing the seeds to the betterment of all beings. Keep it positive, and the results will be—positive!

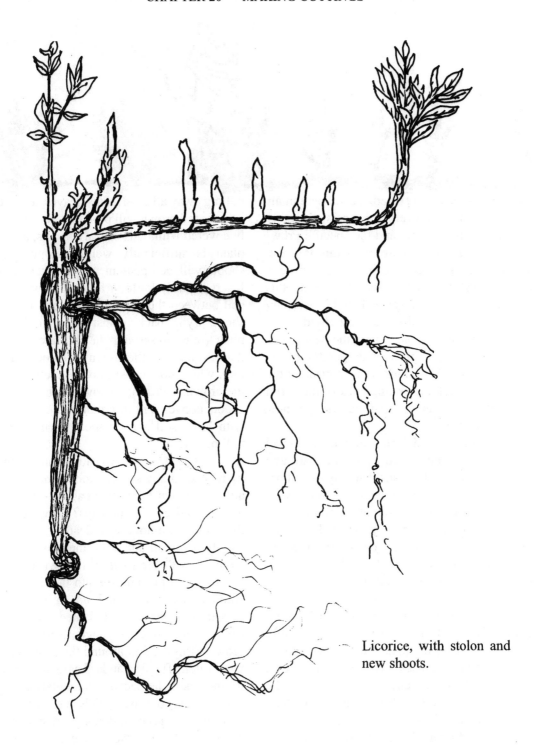

Licorice, with stolon and new shoots.

CHAPTER 20 — MAKING CUTTINGS

Field divisions. Most herbaceous perennials need to be divided every few years. It really depends on the species and the specific growing conditions as to how often this is done. When perennials seem to have reached peak performance (that is, they look less robust this year than they did last year), then it is probably time to rejuvenate the plant by dividing it. Start by preparing a site where the new plants will grow well, a place with good fertility, water, and sun. Divisions are best made in the fall after harvest and cutting back of the aerial portions, or in the spring before the new growth burgeons.

One method is to cut with a shovel straight down into the crown of the plant and lever out chunky divisions that way (see illustration, above). Another method is to dig with a shovel or garden fork around the perimeter of the dormant crown and pry up until you can lever the entire root ball out of the ground. Pick it up and give it a shake to dislodge loose soil. Turn the root upside down in the hole. The buds will now be protected in soft soil, and the roots will be sticking straight up toward you. Using snips, a sharp knife, machete, shovel, or spade, cut the crown into sections from the back side toward the buds. Cut most of the way through, and then pry the crown apart. Cutting from behind and then pulling apart by hand helps prevent damage to the buds. Most mature plants will produce at least 4 strong divisions.

Alternatively, as long as the mother plant is healthy and robust, smaller cuttings may be removed without digging up the entire plant. Clear out around the crown of the plant,

pulling away all dead stems, leaves, and weeds. The central crown will probably be very densely covered with buds or leafy shoots, and if the plant is sufficiently well-developed, lateral shoots will be apparent at the outer margins. Insert a sturdy knife or a spade down into the soil between the central crown and the lateral shoot, prying back against the main part of the plant (thus preserving the delicate hair roots that reside under the crown). Dislodge the cutting, which now consists of a severed piece of the crown with roots below and buds or leafy shoots above. Fill in around the mother plant with loose soil and compost, then mulch. It will be fine.

Clean up the divisions and/or cuttings by removing any severed roots, and especially any weeds that might be attached—things like grasses and clovers perhaps? Anyway, weed them out. Remove any dead or excessively woody material, and plant the newly vitalized cuttings, with the roots well down in the soil and the buds peeping up into the light. Small cuttings may be potted up in gallon pots. Larger divisions are best planted out in the garden or field. Give each plant plenty of room to grow. Firm the soil around the roots and provide water. This is standard gardening practice for increasing herbaceous perennials and short-lived herbaceous perennials, especially those with spreading root systems. I often make field divisions of: boneset, bergamot, comfrey, *Echinacea purpurea*, herbaceous peonies, gravel root, meadowsweet, motherwort, wood betony, and Saint John's wort.

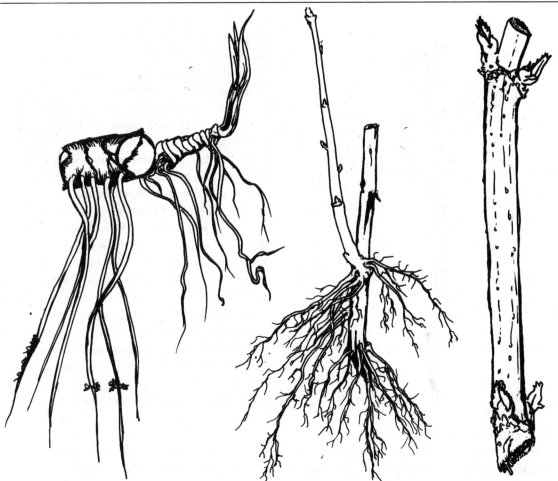

Root cuttings consist of a piece of the rhizome that has reproductive buds or eyes (visible or sometimes microscopic) that will give rise to a new plant. A really good cutting will consist of rootlets, a chunk of rhizome, and a large bud or shoot (see calamus root cutting above on the left). Another good example of an herb that propagates easily by way of root cuttings is Chinese foxglove (*Rehmannia glutinosa*). This plant is difficult to start from seed, but possesses a rubbery underground root system that is loaded with bumpy reproductive nodes. Simply snip a piece of the root and plant it in good soil in a gallon pot left in the greenhouse, or plant it in sandy soil in a sunny garden bed. Orient the cutting horizontally 3 inches below the surface, firm in, and keep warm and evenly moist until the root sends up new aerial parts.

Woody cuttings of bushes and trees consist of a short piece of the 1- to 2-year-old wood, snipped just below one set of buds and just above another. The illustration in the middle shows a depotted cutting of eleuthero that was stuck (planted) in the fall and in time put forth roots and a handsome new shoot. The illustration on the right shows a proper stem cutting of elderberry. To plant a cutting of this sort, prepare a gallon pot full of fluffy, moisture-retentive potting soil and stick the cutting in, with one set of buds below the surface and one set above the surface. Do not stick the cutting all the way to the bottom of the pot, or there will be little room left for root development. Keep the pot in cool, moist shade. New roots will strike down from the base of the cutting, and new stems and leaves will eventually rise up from the buds. Cramp bark and hawthorn can also be propagated in this manner.

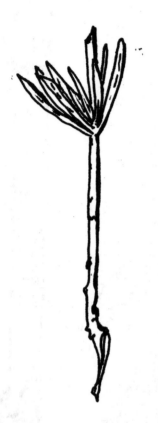

Stem cuttings. Cuttings of lavender, sage, rosemary, and thyme are best made in the fall. Choose a medium-size branch (1 or 2 years old) and, grasping it firmly so as not to injure the stem, break it down and away from the parent plant. This will leave a heel on the cutting where it once was attached to the main stem. Further prepare the cutting by snipping off the tip and basal branches, preserving only a single set of opposing leaves still adhering to the wood. Good cuttings measure 3 inches long, consisting of the heel, the stem, and a single, healthy set of leaves (see illustration of a rosemary cutting, above).

Fill a flat with moist sand and stick cuttings $1^1/_2$ inches deep into the sand, heel down, with the leaves slightly above the surface. Pinch the soil in at the base of each cutting to exclude air pockets. Put the flat on a bench in the greenhouse and erect a plastic tent around it. This is fairly easy to do by tucking a sheet of plastic under the edges of the flat or flats and lifting the center of the plastic tent up

with a string. You can get a grip on the apex of the plastic tent by tying up a small, round pebble into the peak with the string. Tie the other end of the string up to the purlins or the rafters of the greenhouse, pulling it tight, making a little circus tent for your flat of cuttings. This extra plastic tent will maintain a moist, warm environment that is conducive to rooting and keeps the delicate aerial portions of the cutting hydrated and green. Water that evaporates up out of the flat will condense on the inside of the plastic and rain back down on the cuttings.

If you do this right, you will water the flat once after planting (a good time to use willow tea—see page 134) and water again only if the flat dries out. Check it a few times through the winter and if the sand is getting dry, then water it. In the spring, before the greenhouse gets too hot, remove the plastic and you will find that your cuttings resist when you gently tug up on them. This is because they are held into the sand with their spiffy new roots! Dig them up out of the sand, tease them apart, and plant individually into gallon pots. Give them standard, fast-draining potting soil and take care of them until they grow sturdy enough to plant out to the garden.

Forest divisions. Rhizomes are not only about storage—they are also reproductive structures. An average dormant crown of black cohosh, for instance, will have several large buds emerging at the side. Divisions of the dormant root usually consist of a slice of the rhizome with at least one bud, subtended by a reasonable bush of feeder roots. If the cutting looks like this (see left hand illustration on opposite page), then survival is almost assured.

Although a cutting with a large bud is preferred, rhizome cuttings made without any apparent buds may also work well. The typical piece of dormant rhizome contains tiny reproductive eyes that, under the right conditions, can be stimulated to produce buds and stems. If a piece of the rhizome is cut off with a knife and replanted in good soil, then in many cases one of the eyes close to the cut will begin to

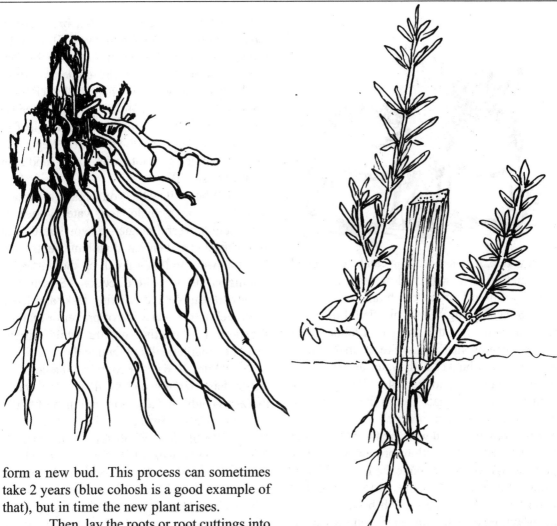

form a new bud. This process can sometimes take 2 years (blue cohosh is a good example of that), but in time the new plant arises.

Then, lay the roots or root cuttings into the furrow, closer together (6 inches) for small plants, and further apart (1 foot) for large plants. Plant the roots with the rootlets down, rhizomes horizontal, buds pointing up, firming them in individually and orienting them with care. Next, cover the roots with soil, firm again around each root, smooth out the surface, and tamp the bed securely with both hands. Finally, distribute the mound of mulch back over the surface. At this point, I personally like to say a prayer over all for safekeeping, until in spring do they wake! If rain is not forthcoming, then it is a good idea to water in the roots. Mark the planting with a stake in order to keep track of where it is. Those emergent buds are very delicate, and a footstep can do a lot of damage!

Layering. Lateral branches of certain herbs and woody perennials (e.g. rosemary, sage, chaste tree, and cramp bark) will make roots if they are pushed down into the soil and held there for 1 or 2 seasons. Choose a lower branch, strip the leaves and any small branches off of the portion that will be buried, and then stake the branch down into the ground, covering a section at least 6 inches long with soil. Leave the branch attached to the mother plant, and leave the leafy tip of the branch arching up out of the soil, into the light. The branch will eventually make roots and, once this occurs, may be severed from the mother plant and potted up or replanted at a distance. A plant propagated in this manner will be a clone of the mother.

Willow tea. Any new cutting can be enlivened by watering it in with willow tea. Snip the growing tips off of willow branches, making them 6 inches long. Cut a big fistful of them, and bundle them with a string or a rubber band into something that looks like a small whisk broom. Fill a bucket with water and immerse the willow broom into the water. Put the bucket in a warm, light place like in the greenhouse or in the sun on the front porch.

Any time you walk by the bucket, feel free to pick up the willow broom and vigorously whisk the water inside the bucket. Whip in as much air as possible. Meanwhile, the willow tips will exude growth hormones into the water, making hormone tea. The whisking will keep the water fresh and not stagnant.

After a week or so, the tea is done. Use it sparingly to water in your root, crown, or stem cuttings. They will respond by creating lots of hair roots, which is just what they need and what you want.

Comfrey leaf tea. The most effective and environmentally friendly plant nutrient I have ever discovered is comfrey leaf tea, a completely home-based, vegetarian, free-of-cost, and nonviolent source of nutrition for plants. Comfrey leaf has a high protein content (10% to 30% protein, based on the dry leaf matter). By brewing fresh comfrey leaves in sun tea, this protein is converted into bioavailable plant nutrients, and it's really good stuff!

First, you get a bucket or barrel, fill it loosely with fresh comfrey leaves, fill it to the brim with water, and then let it steep in the sun. Every morning, you stir the contents with a stick, first one way and then the other. For starters, this stirring will be difficult, because you have to get all that green comfrey leaf in motion, but later, as the comfrey begins to break down, it gets a lot easier to stir (and a lot stinkier to smell).

When you stir, you create a vortex. Related to the tornado, the water vortex is extremely powerful magic—as you stir, the tea is oxygenated and enriched with nutrients. Stir first one way, and then break up the vortex by stirring in the opposite direction. Stirring the tea is a repetitive and relaxing task, and lends itself well to the recitation of prayer or mantra. I believe that reciting mantra while stirring serves to energetically potentize the tea.

After 10 days or so, when the comfrey leaves have largely dissolved into the water, the tea is ready, and at this point it is best to use it without delay. Set up a 3-foot tripod with a large piece of cheesecloth for a filter. Under the filter, put a bucket to catch the filtered tea. Then, dip some raw tea out of the barrel and pour it through the filter. The finished tea will catch in the bucket. Dilute this tea with water before use. Combine equal parts tea and plain water.

Water your plants with the dilute tea, either by spraying as a foliar feed or simply by using a watering can, dousing the leaves, and allowing the life-giving tea to drip down into the roots. I like to starve the plants for water for 1 or 2 days before doing this, then apply the tea, and then let them work on the tea for another 1 or 2 days before watering again with pure water. This is particularly good for nourishing potted plants, plants that are weak or sickly, for watering in new transplants, and for watering field crops that need an extra boost. The plants will be fortified against insect pests, they will grow faster, and they will green up.

CHAPTER 21 — CARING FOR PLANTS

In the late winter, way back in Chapter 16, remember how we started those seeds in the greenhouse? Well, now it's early spring, and those seedlings are sizing up and need to be transplanted to the open garden. A good approach is to take note of the frost-sensitivity of the plants, and begin with the frost-tolerant ones, such as: angelica, bergamot, echinacea, and Roman chamomile. These can be transplanted outdoors a few weeks before the last frost. Plants of this sort will thrive in cool, moist soil.

Later, after the soil warms up, the time arrives to transplant out the heat-loving plants, such as: ashwagandha, basil, bitter melon, and peppers. For these to thrive, the ground should feel hot to the touch at midday. You must take precautions to make sure your little charges are not stressed by the heat or frozen in a late frost.

Hardening-off. It is a good practice to harden-off plants before transplanting them. Sometimes gardeners use a cold frame to toughen-up sensitive young seedlings before transplanting them to outdoor conditions. A simpler method is to wait until a few days before transplant, then place the flat of seedlings outdoors where the sun and wind can toughen the plants.

Set the flat somewhere close to where the plants will be planted. This is often a newly forked or tilled bed, so it will be easy to find a spot to dig a shallow trench, settle the flat into the depression, and then hill up the soil around the sides of the flat. The trench will protect the plants from excessive heat, keep them from drying out during the hardening-off period, and give them a lower profile to help reduce wind stress. Leave them out there in the field for a few days. They will toughen-up. If the plants start to dry out, for goodness' sake, water them.

Once the plants are sufficiently accustomed to outdoor conditions, then depot them and plant them. Do this in the early morning, in the evening, or on a cloudy day. The soil in the pot ought to be moist at transplant. After transplanting, always give the plant a drink of water. This integrates the roots with the soil.

Depot the plant by inverting it onto your hand. Keep your palm flat on the soil in the pot when you turn it over, with the stem of the plant supported between your fingers. If the plant doesn't slide right out onto your hand, then give a strong, even downward plunge interrupted by a sharp upward pull on the pot (see illustration). Catch the block of soil and roots when the plant comes sliding precipitously out. This is the most stress-free way to remove plants from plastic pots, although I've observed that not all gardeners know this trick. It's a good one.

Regardless of how you get the plant out of the pot, it is not a good idea to strike the bottom of the pot with your hand or a tool—percussive vibrations are traumatic to the hair roots and will shock the plant. If the plant is stuck in the pot and won't come out, then flex the bottom of the pot with your thumbs and try to pop out the root ball that way.

In extreme cases, the roots may be swelling out of the pot like a body builder's pectorals in a too-small tank top. In this case, it may require a razor knife to cut the pot into pieces, which can then be peeled away from the roots. This is always a big relief, I think, for the plant.

Briefly examine the roots. If the roots are pot-bound (having wrapped around and around the inside of the pot, looking for nutrients, seeking egress) then it will be best to free up the roots before planting. You can break the block of soil apart, gently removing the old soil from around the root system. Give the plant a gentle shake to unwind the roots. To avoid whiplash, always hold the plant by the crown, and support the stem between your fingers. Remove and discard any rotten roots. Allow the newly freed, lively roots to hang down, assuming a more natural shape.

As above so below. Now consider pruning. Ideally, the mass of the aerial parts will match the mass of the roots. If the roots seem overly long in comparison to the aerial parts, or if they are so long that it will be difficult to dig a hole deep enough to accommodate them, then trim them back with a pair of snippers or heavy-duty scissors. Within reason, feeder roots can be pruned back without a worry (this will stimulate their healthy regrowth in the new soil), but snipping off the bottom of heavy taproots is not a good idea, as this can leave an inroad for disease, shock the plant, or even kill it.

If the roots are small and the aerial parts are tall and leggy, then prune the aerial parts. Observe the buds or leaves on the stem, and make your cut just above some really healthy ones. Remove any dead stems or leaves. Trimming may look drastic right now, but when done prudently, it is a practice that improves survival at transplant. Pruning eventually yields great rewards, including bushier growth and greater vigor.

136

Transplanting. Now the plant is ready to be transplanted. Given a newly forked bed or a newly tilled field, my tool of choice for transplanting is the spade. Maybe it's the tree planter coming out in me, but I really like to plant by sticking the shovel directly into the prepared ground and then gently pulling up and back on the loose soil, opening up a deep hole into the earth, the loose soil still held back by my spade. Then, grasping the plant in my left hand by the crown or the base of the stem, I dangle the roots down in the hole and give them a bit of a jiggle to help them assume a natural posture, briefly checking to make sure that I like the planting depth. At this point, I quickly lift the spade out of the hole, allowing the loose soil to fall back down around the roots of the plant, locking them in this natural position, the tips of the roots deep within the earth, the crown at the level of the soil surface.

Check the height of planting, and if the plant is too high in the hole, then gently remove it and try again. If the plant is too low, then gently work your hand down below the roots and lift the plant until it is at exactly the right level. If done properly, there is very little extra filling in needed, but of course you really aren't done planting until you set your spade to the side and stick your hands down into the soil around the roots of the plant, making sure that the soil compacts nicely around them, and that there are no air pockets. Fill in around the stem, tamp securely, and cultivate the surface soil to smoothness with your hands. Rubber fingers again. Make wide sweeping motions on the surface of the earth.

Think good thoughts about the medicine, who it will help and how it will work. Go on and plant more plants. Water them in. To reduce transplant shock, you can mix a handful of dried kelp in with the water in the watering can or bucket. After all this, leave the plants alone and forget about them for a full day. They've had plenty of attention (too much attention) and they need to compose themselves. Gardening is about the pauses—doing and not doing. After this pause, return and make sure your little charges are standing upright and if necessary further buttress them against the wind by heaping soil around them, and water them again. In short, make sure they are digging in—and they will be.

Have you ever stopped to view the world from the perspective of the plants? How do plants perceive? What is their information gathering process, and what makes them respond as they do? Well, many explanations have been proposed, from the scientific model of chemical messaging to the metaphysical model of plant spirit.

I've observed that plants are on a slower time frame than humans, and yet, like humans, they are tactile beings. When a vine touches a string, it spirals around to grab hold of it. We don't see this movement because of the anthropocentric rapidity of our perceptions.

Below ground, the root reaches out for a texture not too muddy or too dry, feeling its way through soft zones where there is oxygen, water, and food. We know this because when we dig up plants, we see what kind of soil their roots have chosen to colonize. Plants perceive the world by way of slow touch, texture, sun, and water. We needn't anthropomorphize them—they are their own unique kind of feeling being.

Spacing of plants. The practical way to view plant spacing is that one thins or transplants in such a way that the plants, upon reaching full size, just touch outer leaves, one with another. This is known as self-mulching, a practice that makes good use of total nutrient and light availability while protecting the living soil from the sun. Planting in triangles is the best way to achieve this effect, providing optimal

plant density and maximizing space for growth. Another advantage of planting in triangles is that the grouping of three plants can be tied together into a sturdy, self-supporting tripod if they get top-heavy. This will secure them against the wind and keep the flowers and seeds up off the soil, clean and dry. This is a good trick.

Plant spacing can have significant impact on water requirements, photosynthesis, nutrient availability, and yield. In desert or dry-land farming conditions, it makes sense to space the plants further apart to reduce competition for available water resources (e.g. the way the Hopi people grow corn). Mulch the surface of the soil to protect it from the sun.

In low-light areas, it also makes sense to plant further apart, because otherwise the plants will compete with each other for light. This phenomenon can be seen when the gardener plants tomatoes or the related plant, goldenberry, too closely. You get lots of leaves, but very little fruit. When planting medicinal herbs for leaf production, such as: agrimony, chicory, chickweed, common mugwort, and wild dandelion, then the plants can be set more closely together. They will shade each other and produce plenty of fresh leaves with a delayed onset of flowering.

In a full sun situation, plants with harvestable taproots, such as gobo burdock and *Echinacea angustifolia,* can be left at very close spacing—4 inches apart in the row—in order to optimize root production. Plants with spreading root systems, such as: *Echinacea purpurea,* elecampane, feverfew, motherwort, and marshmallow, ought to be planted so that, upon maturity, the outer leaves just touch— plant to plant.

Plant spacing has an impact on resistance to stressors. In the forest, it makes sense to distance the plants slightly further apart, so that they do not touch leaves. This more closely resembles the way these plants grow in nature, reduces competition for light, increases root yield, and especially in the case of American ginseng reduces the potential for disease transfer from one plant to another.

In essence, organic plantings are best maintained at a greater spacing (less plants per given area) than what is normally seen in commercial agriculture—we have no chemical fertilizer or insecticide inputs to uphold an unnaturally dense planting. What we do have is a gentle availability of nutrients and robust plants that are naturally resistant to insect pests. Furthermore, the admixture of species in a diverse habitat, achieved by planting blocks of different species instead of a monocrop, further improves resistance to the spread of pathogens, confuses browsers, and initiates a balanced relationship between all insects, including those that we perceive as pests and those that we perceive to be beneficial.

Bringing plants in for the winter. If you're growing a biennial or perennial herb that does fine during the summer, but definitely won't make it through your winter, then you do have the option of pruning back and repotting (usually into a gallon pot or larger) and bringing the plant indoors for the winter. If you have a heated greenhouse or an indoor room that is warm and light, then this practice can yield some good returns. For instance, I've overwintered Kilimanjaro basil (a woody bush basil from the tropics) indoors, protecting the plants from snow and frost, then planted them out in the spring, and harvested copious quantities of seeds in this manner (many tropical plants require 2 growing seasons before they will make seed). For me, this method is standard practice for maintaining some of my strains of tropical and subtropical plants, such as: balm

of Gilead, brahmi, gotu kola, and Mayan mint. I also make sure to bring in some of my larger white sage plants, as they are not guaranteed to survive the winter outdoors in my area. I dearly love them, and it's well worth the extra effort. All these plants do fine in the summer garden, and once they are potted up and brought indoors for the winter, they can be maintained by keeping them warm, in the light, and infrequently watered. Then, we can plant them outdoors again in the spring. Another option is to make cuttings, work them up in the greenhouse, and plant them out to the garden once conditions are again conducive.

Preparing outdoor plants for winter. Since the majority of medicinal herbs are herbaceous perennials, their care and upkeep is a year 'round process. Gardeners do a lot of weeding and futzing in the spring and then tend to give the garden less attention in the fall. Once the apples hang heavy on the tree, the school bell starts to ring, and the flowers begin to fade, our enthusiasm for gardening diminishes. After all, the fruits of our labors are preserved in the pantry. Many herbs are hanging dry in the rafters, and the apothecary shelf is heavy with new tinctures and salves.

A little attention to the plant habitat in the fall will make the spring garden better. One final time, go into the garden and cut back any

remaining stalks from the perennials, such as: gravel root, elecampane, and nettles. Toss the stalks in the carbon pile. You will probably see nascent buds and leaves there at the crown of the plant. Think about how easy it is to find these plants right now and how hard it will be to find them in the spring, after winter renders them unrecognizable.

Stir up the soil around the crowns with rubber fingers. Remove small weeds, clovers, and grasses that would otherwise take root through the winter. Mulch the crowns with about 4 inches of mulch, less mulch in warm winter areas, more in cold winter areas. Use inert mulch, such as: rotted sawdust, leaves, straw, or hydrated coir—not compost. You don't want to stimulate new growth; you want to put the plants to bed. In the spring, you'll wear a smile as the new leaves push up brightly through their cushy bed, unharmed by the icy and cloven foot of winter.

Autumn is also a good time to attend to last-minute cleanups and pickups, including the cutoff pieces from those boards you used on the greenhouse door, the pile of reject cardboard that never became weed barrier, and an alarming array of plastic and terra-cotta pots,

shards, and odds-and-ends that have spilled out from the potting shed. Everything gets put away before the snow, because truth be told random garbage is as ugly as a flower is pretty, and items left lying on the ground become habitat for slugs and snails.

Make good use of those autumn tree leaves! It is a travesty to burn them or send them to the dump! Piles of leaves can be layered in the compost pile or left to decompose. Come spring, you will certainly appreciate the mulch.

In the fall, literally all the forest medicinal roots, such as: black cohosh, goldenseal, and trillium, as well as some of the woody perennials, such as elderberry or tree peony, are far from dormant. As the weather cools, they send out soft, whitish feeder roots, sucking resources into the rhizome, creating a foundation for next year's growth. With the fall rains, the overwintering annuals, such as milk thistle and lobelia, are seeding in and quickly developing basal rosettes. These may be thinned and weeded at this time of year, which will set them up for improved yield early the following summer.

Plants that flower in the winter. Around here, there are a few plants that actually bulk up, thrive, and sometimes even flower in the late fall and in the winter. In this class I would put: Himalayan sarcococca, witch hazel (see below), horny goat weed, violets, my precious mandrakes, and black hellebore.

Regarding the maturation of gardens. There is a wise Cherokee adage recommending that in order to develop the right conduct for protecting the earth, one should act for the benefit of people living seven generations in the future. I try to employ this approach in my gardening, as it helps me to have patience and to give as much as I can, because I know it's not mine.

In the temperate zone, at least, garden annuals birthe and die within the space of a few moons. Perennials also show marked changes as they progress from spring buds to autumn seeds. Most plants mature a lot faster than do people. This means that in the space of a human lifetime, each of us gardeners has the opportunity to completely transform the land by growing plants and trees.

Right from the start, a gardener would like to have the perspective to visualize the garden as it will be seven years in the future. Instead most of us have to guess which perennials will become extremely large, how big the trees will actually grow, what plants will learn to self-seed and naturalize, and which ones will need to be continually reintroduced in order to derive the benefits. If we are fortunate, then we actually get to see how it all turns out. Given that change is gradual and we become inured to our surroundings as change occurs, then it can be illuminating indeed to dig out those old panoramic photos of the gardens.

I watch the myriad pollinators, backlighted by a westering sun, swarming the open flowers of a hawthorn that I remember planting long ago from seed. Roses once coddled and coerced have become impenetrable walls of flowering thorns. Vines once hand-trained to the trellis have *become* the trellis, showering flowers like jewels. California poppies and Flanders poppies, once hand-planted in rows and given compost, now rise up voluntarily in weed-free, bicolor stands that look like they belong in a magazine. And, we certainly don't have to plant burdock anymore . . .

Yes, by creating habitat and planting trees and perennials, and by naturalizing different populations of annual herbs and weeds, then we are improving things for the next generation. By planting trees, surely we will improve the earth for seven generations in the future. Over the years, older plants and trees seem to gain their independence, needing less and less human assistance to grow and thrive. The gardener can rest more, and eat cherries right off the twig.

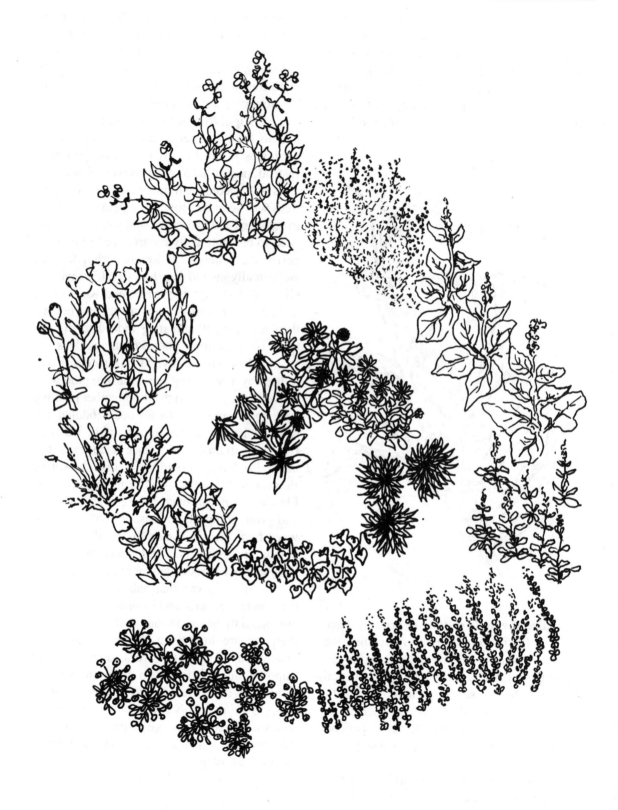

ADDENDUMS

A: SEED PRODUCTION

B: HARVESTING & PROCESSING MEDICINAL HERBS

ADDENDUM A : SEED PRODUCTION

Raising medicinal herbs for production of seeds requires an understanding of pollination, plant growth cycles, growing season, water management, harvest, and processing. For the purpose of seed production, plants can be usefully categorized as either "outcrossers" (those that send their pollen out into the world to find a receptively sticky stigma, such as echinacea) and "selfers" (those that are self-fertile, such as wild indigo).

The minimum number of plants required to achieve healthy genetic diversity of the offspring will be very different depending on whether one is growing outcrossers or selfers. The kind of seed-saving I am recommending here is meant to maintain the plants in their original wild form and, therefore, differs substantially from current plant-breeding models that rely on selection, hybridization, or genetic engineering. Seed-saving is a gentle practice of guiding small populations of healthy parent plants to produce offspring that closely resemble the parents, year after year. This process is made possible by what is known as "open-pollination," where plants are self-pollinated or pollinated by wind, insects, birds, or animals—not by human manipulation.

Outcrossing plants, such as most members of the aster and carrot families, require a mixture of many parent individuals to produce seed that produces a stable population. In practice, this means that instead of growing 12 plants for the purpose of saving seeds, it would be better to grow 1,200 plants. One can get by with growing fewer individuals, and the integrity of the seed will probably not suffer too much, but the result of growing too few individuals for multiple seasons would be inbreeding depression. Inbreeding depression generally takes the form of aberrant flower form, dwarfism, a lack of vigor, a diminution of medicinal compounds, and/or decreased yield. The antidote to inbreeding depression is known as outbreeding enhancement, the practice of bringing in new seed from a different population to diversify the genetics of a stand of cultivated plants.

Chance hybridization. Another challenge with outcrossing plants is that they can hybridize with other species in the same genus (as long as they are flowering at the same time, that is). For example, growing blocks of plants of *Echinacea angustifolia* and *Echinacea purpurea* too closely together could produce random hybrids. Bees would move the pollen from one species to another. Technically, this is not supposed to happen, since one of the defining characteristics of a true species is that it will not accept pollen from a plant of a different species, but in practice it *does* happen.

There are a few relevant methods for disallowing this sort of unintentional, random, and probably unhelpful hybridization. One method is isolation. Plants that freely hybridize are best grown at a distance from related species, in order to assure that the off-spring are true. For instance, when planting echinacea or tulsi for seed, grow as many individuals as possible and space the patches at least 100 feet apart. These plants are from the aster and the mint families, which tend to be enthusiastic outcrossers.

Isolation is not only a function of distance, but of ecology. Examples of ecological barriers to hybridization would be a ravine, a line of trees, or a grouping of dissimilar plants. Any or all of these features, singly or in combination, can help keep the genetics consistent.

Another kind of physical barrier to hybridization would be a floating row cover (available from local nurseries). This is basically a fabric that can be draped over the plants. It helps extend the season and may keep pollination more localized.

Staggering of plantings. Excellent results may be achieved by timing the planting of similar crops so that they do not flower in concert. For instance, a fall-planted field of *Echinacea angustifolia* will flower in the early summer, and a spring-planted field of *Echinacea purpurea* will flower in the autumn. Such

fields could be located right next to each other without raising concerns about hybridization, because the flowers would mature at different times, and the resulting seeds would be true to species.

Of course, if the plants were left in the field for another year, they would then all flower at more or less the same time. In this case, the medicine produced by the roots would be typical to the individual species, but the seed itself might take on characteristics of the other species. In other words, the root harvest for medicine would be dependable, but the seed harvest for replanting would not.

Examples of enthusiastic outcrossers. Other medicinal herbs that will hybridize between cultivars or species unless sufficient physical, spatial, or temporal separation is employed are: lavender, mint, motherwort, oregano, sage, and skullcap, which are all members of the mint (*Lamiaceae*) family; bitter melon, cucumber, and gourd, which are all members of the cucumber (*Cucurbitaceae*) family; boneset, chamomile, feverfew, goldenrod, gravel root, marigold, spilanthes, sunflower, and yarrow, which are all members of the aster (*Asteraceae*) family; mullein, in the figwort (*Scrophulariaceae*) family; plantain, in the plantain (*Plantaginaceae*) family; poppy, in the poppy (*Papaveraceae*) family; rhubarb, in the buckwheat (*Polygonaceae*) family; and wild yam in the yam (*Dioscoraceae*) family.

146

Maintaining varietal integrity. Different varieties of basil, such as Thai basil and sweet lettuce leaf basil (both of which are *Ocimum basilicum*) can easily intermix and toss quite a bit of variability into the works. This is especially true if the patches are located too near each other and are visited by the same pollinators. If planting basil for the purpose of seed saving, it is best to provide at least 100 feet between cultivars to help assure genetic purity. Incorporating the concepts of isolation and staggering the plantings is also a good idea.

Self-fertile plants, such as most members of the nightshade (*Solanaceae*) and pea (*Fabaceae)*, do not require outside pollinators to make seed. These plants have perfect flowers, with both male (staminate) and female (pistilate) parts. Self-pollination (autogamy) is where the pollen fertilizes the female part of the same flower or another flower on the same plant. With self-fertile plants, it really doesn't matter how many of them you grow—the seed produced by a few individuals (e.g. 12) is just as reliable as seed produced by many individuals.

Apomictic (asexual) plants, such as agrimony, dandelion, and hawthorn, do not require pollination in order to make viable seed. Instead, the embryo of the seed arises from an unfertilized egg within the embryo sac (via modified meiosis). Plants of this sort remain the same from year to year, so again it doesn't matter how many of them you grow—the seed from one apomictic plant will be just as useful as the seed from another, or from many. Plants of this sort discovered long ago that their genetic makeup was more or less universally successful and, like saffron-robed monks, they then took the vow of celibacy in order to better serve us all. Dandelions are holy.

Selecting for vigor is always a good idea. The largest, healthiest, fastest-germinating seedlings are the ones we choose to save, and any weak or spindly seedlings are weeded out. As mentioned previously, we rogue any plants that present atypical flowers, are weak or sickly, or for some reason seem like they will not make good medicine. The sickly seedlings and plants are not missed, and this practice just makes more room for the healthy ones to grow and prosper.

Selecting for specific traits. One rainy day in March found me in the gentle warmth of my greenhouse, thinning a flat of Krishna tulsi (*Ocimum tenuiflorum*) that sat before me on the bench. The seedlings had emerged in 20 days, stimulated nicely by some bright weather that sent the daytime temperatures inside the greenhouse to 90° F. On this day, the seedlings radiated the buoyant optimism of early life. It was my solemn task to prevent overcrowding by thinning out the weak ones and propping up the best as keepers. I noticed at this time that not only could I keep the largest, most perfectly formed, and most vigorous individuals, but I also had the opportunity to select for color. Some of the vibrant seedlings demonstrated a rich burgundy hue, while the majority looked quite green. Knowing that red coloration in tulsi is an indicator of excellent taste and medicinality, I pulled out the green ones and left the seedlings that demonstrated stronger color. "This," I told myself, "is the way that select cultivars have been produced since the dawn of gardening."

Encourage diverse pollinators. One of the main advantages of planting diversity is that there is always something flowering in the garden, a constant display of color and fragrance that encourages pollinators to reside in the area. Mixed plantings of trees, bushes, woody perennials, herbaceous perennials, cover crops, grasses, and annuals will make food and shelter for a vast number of pollinators, such as: ants, bees, beetles, butterflies, moths, and wasps—seen and unseen. Efficient pollination improves overall seed yield.

Hand-pollination. We use this as a last resort when it appears that a plant is making flowers without producing fruits. These tend to be rare and unusual plants that require a specific pollinator that may not be present. Examples of herbs that may require hand-pollination are mandrake (*Mandragora officinalis*), vanilla (*Vanilla planifolia*), and the beautiful yellow lady's slipper orchid (*Cypripedium calceolus*).

Hand-pollinating flowers in the cucumber (*Cucurbitaceae*), such as jiao-gu-lan (*Gynostemma* spp.), gourds (*Lageneria* spp.), or squash (*Cucurbita* spp.), is a good way to keep them from hybridizing with other members of the cucumber family. Use a soft-haired paintbrush (the kind made for painting with watercolors, not for kind you use for painting a boat). This is best done on a clear day (not rainy) when the flower is fully opened and the pollen is dust-like. Gently brush the pollen from the anther and then transfer the pollen by brushing against the sticky stigma. Some of the male gametes will adhere and gravitate down into the ovary and bingo—you got seeds. Imagine your brush is the hairy abdomen of a bee. Buzzing is optional.

Maintenance of genetic diversity. When saving seed, it is important to make sure that the collection comes from a sufficiently diverse population of parent plants. However, self-pollinating plants in the legume family (*Fabaceae*) or the nightshade family (*Solanaceae*) tend to produce progeny that reflect the attributes of the parents, even if the seed is collected from only a few individuals. For example, when I harvest goat's rue or peppers for seed, I have no qualms about the genetic diversity of the offspring, which remains robust and true, even when seed is taken from a small patch of plants. However, the seed of outcrossing plants from the aster family (*Asteraceae*) or the mint family (*Lamiaceae*) are best collected from many individuals. This assures a healthy representation of all traits, such as: color, disease resistance, frost hardiness, flavor, medicinality, etc.

Grow in blocks. Ask any farmer—it is better to grow 3 rows of corn in a block than 1 row of corn that goes from here to way out there. The reason for this is simple—blocks of plants pollinate more efficiently than rows of plants. If you grow a single row of corn, the ears may have lots of empty spaces where a little male gamete missed its calling, never adhered to a sticky stigma, never slipped in anticipation down that lithe and rubbery tube known as the stile. If you grow the corn in blocks, then the pollen falls down from tassels all around, and the ears grow as fat as chipmunk cheeks. So in medicinal herb farming, we tend to grow in beds consisting of at least 3 rows, with the plants arranged in triangles, giving maximum production in a minimum of space. This arrangement also improves pollination. The number of plants in each block will vary according to the yield required, but for the purpose of seed production it's a good practice to plant at least 12—more, if possible.

Healthy plants produce more seed. Giving plants enough space to grow, watering according to their needs, and providing them with their fair share of compost will ultimately produce a very robust plant that produces plenty of seed. The herban legend that says, "Starve a plant to stimulate a survival response and it'll make more seed." sounds plausible, but in practice I find it to be untrue.

Of course, plants must accomplish maturation of their seeds within the local growing season, or the seed crop will fail. Fertilizing and watering late in the growing season are contraindicated, as this can retard the development of seed. Once the plant begins making seed, it is best to back off on watering, and once the seedpod begins to dry, reduce watering to a minimum—once or twice a week, depending on the weather. At this stage, a moist seedpod can delay maturity, reduce the quality of the seed crop, and in the worst case scenario, promote mold.

Amending during the flowering period with phosphorus-rich organic fertilizer, such as bat guano, can definitely encourage copious flowering and seed production. The Nitrogen-Phosphorous-Potassium (NPK) ratio for bat guano is (3-10-1). The guano is very concentrated and is best diluted with water before using it to fertilize the plant.

Identification becomes an issue when growers fail to keep good records. It is a common human foible to say, "This is a really significant planting in a good spot. I'll remember what I put here." Famous last words. Our memories are not necessarily that good. Record-keeping can be as simple as driving a stake in the ground next to the planting and wiring a metal identification tag to the stake. Tags of this sort can be scribed with a pen or pencil, and the tags remain readable for years. Write the name of the plant and the sow date on the tag.

Another method of keeping track of what was planted where and when is to keep a written garden logbook. Then, if an identity crisis occurs, you can look back in your records and find the name of the plant that you once knew and since forgot. Once you harvest the seed, make absolutely sure that you keep it labeled throughout the process of cleaning, drying, and storage. Put a tag in with the seeds that gives the common and Latin name and the harvest date.

Following these few good practices of cultivation for seed, you can produce a seed lot of great storability and high germination that produces vigorous seedlings well-adapted to conditions in your garden. Your seed strains will remain dependable, resistant to pests, true to form—and the medicine you grow will be strong.

HARVEST AND CLEANING OF SEEDS.

Harvest dry seeds when they are fully mature. Most seeds are soft and light-colored when immature and become harder and darker colored when mature. There are of course exceptions. One of the best ways to determine if a seed is ripe and viable is to grasp it between your two front teeth and gently bite down. I know this sounds like odd advice, but actually it is one of the better tests to differentiate a poor seed from a good seed.

When you bite down on a seed that has a proper testa and endosperm, you can *feel* the vitality of it. Biting a seed that lacks proper resources to sprout feels like your teeth are squishing an empty bag. Of course, this method is not recommended for something big and hard like a field pea or a scarlet emperor bean—you might break a tooth! This method is also not recommended for seeds that contain toxic compounds, such as castor or aconite. However, this test works excellently for small seeds, such as rosemary, goat's rue, or motherwort—even a seed as small as Saint John's wort can be assessed by tooth.

This method is useful in discriminating between mature, fertile seeds and decoys. Decoys *look* like seeds, but are hollow. They are the veritable wooden nickel of plantdom. The survival advantage of producing decoys occurs when the plant tricks an animal into losing interest in its seeds, because the first one doesn't taste like anything much.

Most plants have learned that it makes reproductive sense to hold onto their seeds until they are mature, and then let them go slowly, a few at a time, into the outer environment. During wet weather, the follicle or the capitulum (the seed-holding compartment, as it were) physically closes down around the seed, protecting it from moisture, disallowing its release into the outer environment. For instance, we've learned that it's useless to try to shake Saint John's wort seed out of the seedpod into a bucket on a moist day—the plant won't let go of the seed! The timing of seed harvest is quite critical—you need to observe your plants on an ongoing basis and pick the seed just as it reaches maturity, on a dry day, when the plant starts to let go. Sometimes it can take weeks or even months for a plant to mature all of its seeds, so it makes sense to pick the seeds on an ongoing basis, starting early as the first seeds mature and ending when the main portion of the seeds are completely mature and falling readily from the plant.

There are many unique methods for harvesting seeds, often dependent upon the tools at hand and the individual requirements of the various plants, but the most common method is to wait until the afternoon of a dry day and then invert the stem and its seed heads into a plastic bucket and give it all a good shake. Whack the dried seed heads against the sides of the bucket. Usually the seed will pour out, sometimes mixed with a lot of inert chaff, and sometimes in a relatively pure state.

Using hand-held, graduated seed screens for cleaning seeds. The best screens are made of stainless steel and are small enough (12 inches square) to hold in the hand, but with high enough sides (3 inches) to safely hold 200 grams of seed, more if the seed is heavy and dense. Mesh size should graduate from coarse (1/4 inch = 4 strands per inch) down to very fine (40 strands per inch). Choose the

mesh most applicable to the task at hand. Find the screen that is just barely bigger than the seeds, put a very fine screen underneath it to catch the seeds, and then shake the seeds through the big screen into the small screen. Next, find the screen that is just slightly smaller than the seed, and put the seedy material into that one, and shake out the dust. What you will have left, if you did this right, is the seed and a small amount of chaff that is the same size as the seed. Luckily, this chaff is probably much lighter than the seed, so it can be separated by wind.

How to blow off the seed. Notice that when you jiggle the screen, the chaff rides up on top of the seeds. Still shaking, work the seed and chaff to the inside lip of the screen by tilting the screen down in the front. Do not spill the seeds. At this point, the light chaff can be blown off by delicately passing one's breath over the top of the seed, blowing away the non-seed portions like the wind skimming *meerschaum* (sea foam) off of a wave. This can be an incredibly useful trick, probably requiring an embrasure similar to the one Kokopelli uses to play his flute. Repeat the shaking of the seed and blowing away of the chaff as many times as it appears to be yielding benefit, at which point discontinue, in order to avoid blowing off too much of the good seed and before hyperventilation causes lightheadedness. If the sample appears still insufficiently clean, then it may help to wind-winnow the remainders, as wind-winnowing can sometimes be effective where blowing is not.

Wind-winnowing. Where I am, the wind passes over the landscape in the evenings, and can be a pleasant respite from the heat of autumn. By late autumn, wind also presages rain, reminding me to bring in whatever seeds are ripe before the rain hits. Zephyrs of billowing wind gently bend the lithe green tops of fir trees poking up on the horizon. I see the long, unkempt tufts of fescue bunchgrass bend over in Mr. Barleywater's field. I'm standing in the middle of the yard, having spread out a sheet on the short, green grass. The grass is dry, as it is late afternoon.

Now the wind prickles the hairs on my arms, and my nostrils dilate in anticipation. I'm holding the rim of a bucket of finely ground chaff and seeds in one hand, and an empty #3 screen (9 strands per inch) in the other hand. A #3 screen is pretty wide and will let most everything I have in my bucket pass through, but it will interrupt the pile of chaff sufficiently to cause a saltshaker effect, a sifting of the contents, with particles coming down like rain, not like a sheet of water. This helps, as it gives the passing wind (which has now expressed itself as a lifting sensation that brings the smell of roses from the gate and flutters the edge of the sheet) the requisite space to propel each little bit of chaff downwind, producing a dancing cloud of non-seed debris that lands somewhere in the grasses. The seeds themselves hit the sheet like hail on a sidewalk, and a broad smile interrupts my concentration. After the last bit of chaffy seed has been relinquished to the wind, I toss aside my tools and quickly gather up the sheet.

I hear something, a rising muted howl in the fir trees, and I can tell by the bending of their tops that a bigger gust is coming on the heels of the first. Dumping the seed back into the empty bucket, I give it a swirl and check it out. It's shiny and black and it is clean enough for me for now. The wind is fluttering my shirt as I carry everything back inside the shed and pour the seed out on a #7 screen (22 strands per inch), which keeps it secure, but allows for further drying. I write out a label that reads: white sage, *Salvia apiana,* organic, date such-and-such, and put my initials. Then I set the screen aside on a table and go do something else.

The next day I return and give the seed a stir with my fingers—definitely rubber fingers. I can tell that it is a bit dryer than it was the day before. I return each day and stir the seed again. This is the process of curing the seed, and it is a step that should not be skipped, as this practice vastly improves the quality of the seed. It has to do with even and complete dehydration. As I stir, I sometimes lift the screen to my pursed lips and blow across the top of the seed to remove the last of the chaff. The shed is warm and well-ventilated.

Table separation. This is most effective for medium and large seeds. When none of the other methods really seem to work, when the wind won't blow right and the chaff doesn't want to rise to the surface when you shake the seed in a screen, sometimes table sorting is the only option remaining. Pour the seed out on the table and paw through it, starting at the edge closest to you, sliding the seeds into one pile and pushing the chaff off to the side. Do not pick through the pile to pull out seeds—it's better to work systematically, which gives a good result and really helps you know when enough is enough.

Flotation. Seeds in fleshy fruits can usually be cleaned by thoroughly smashing the fruits (do not add water yet) on a screen or in a cloth bag. The bag works really well—you introduce the fresh fruit (e.g. ashwagandha, cascara sagrada, elderberry, goldenseal, jack-in-the-pulpit, Solomon's seal, and trillium), tightly close the top of the bag with a string, and smash and knead the bag with your hands. Then introduce the mash (smashed fruit and seeds) into a bucket, and pour plenty of clean, cold water over the mass to break it up. Agitate, then swirl in a circular motion, let the bucket contents settle for a few seconds and finally, at precisely the best moment, pour the nonseed portions off the top, leaving the seeds behind in the bottom of the bucket.

This method is known as decanting, and the entire process is known as flotation. The skin and pulp of the berry stay suspended in the water, while the seed sinks to the bottom of the bucket. Several changes of water and careful decanting to pour away the nonseed portion will wash and purify the seed, also separating nonviable seed (which usually but not always floats) from viable seed (which usually sinks).

Don't throw the baby out with the bathwater, but change the water enough times to make sure that the baby is really clean. Once the heavy, viable seed is visible as a mass in the bottom of the bucket, go ahead and pour it all at once into a screen or sieve that is too small for the seed to pass through. The water will flow away and the seed will be left behind like a salmon in a net. At this point, depending on the specific species and its tolerance of dry storage, you can either replant the seed immediately, store it in moist medium (sand or coir) in the refrigerator until it is convenient, prudent, or seasonally appropriate to plant it, or slow-dry the seed on a screen (positive airflow, less than 90° F, stir daily until dry).

Fermentation. Seeds of various fruits and berries, such as: bilberry, elderberry, poke, persimmon and tomato, are surrounded by fleshy or gelatinous tissue that needs to be removed before the seed can be finished by flotation. One excellent method of efficiently breaking down this tissue is known as fermentation, where the fruits are smashed and mixed with a little water in a loosely-lidded bucket and allowed to sit in a warm place for 1 to 3 days. The mash is stirred 2 times per day, and will bubble and froth as it works. Do not leave the mash longer than 3 days, or the seed may discolor and lose its viability. Judiciously employed, fermentation improves seed germination and shelf life.

Preserving seeds within the semi-dried berry. Certain seeds, such as angelica tree, elderberry, and the aforementioned goji berry and schisandra will last for years if stored in the dried or semi-dried (raisiny) berry, but do not last long once removed from the fruit and exposed to the air. The flesh of the berry is germination inhibiting and preservative, holding the seed in a state of suspended animation.

In order to produce the dried berry, wait until the fruit is fully ripe and pick the entire fruit cluster. Dry the fruit on the stem, on screens in an area where there is positive air flow. Turn the fruit often to dry evenly, and never allow the temperature to exceed 90° F. Once the berries dry to a raisiny consistency, they may be rubbed and separated from the stem by passing them through a screen or by rolling them down an inclined plane. The berries may be further dried until nearly hard, then stored in paper bags in a cool, dry place. Check the berries frequently to be sure they are not rehydrating or beginning to mold.

Packaging and lot numbering of dried seed. After a week or two of curing, the dried seed will be ready for storage. Pour the seed into a paper envelope and label it appropriately. A piece of paper folded once in the center and then reopened is an excellent tool for seed transfers. Spread the paper flat on a table, pour the seed into the center of the paper in a pile, then lift up the sides of the paper, and funnel the seed into the envelope—very nifty. Home gardeners need simply label the packet with herb name and harvest year. Other useful information would include the Latin name, organic status, seed weight, and lot number. The lot number corresponds to your notes about the harvest, kept in a logbook.

Storage of dried medicinal herb seed. Dried seed can be stored very nicely in paper bags or paper envelopes. Cellophane bags, plastic bags, and glass jars can also be quite serviceable. Cotton drawstring bags or woven plastic bags are excellent for storing larger harvests, such as amaranth, beans, or sunflower seeds. The seed must be thoroughly dried and cured before putting it away, otherwise it can easily sweat and rot during storage. Furthermore, before putting it away, the seed is best cleaned, so that it is relatively free of chaff, because chaff is dead material that sometimes attracts moisture and molds that damage the seed.

Properly dehydrated medicinal herb seeds of the common sort (e.g. arnica, borage, basil, motherwort, thyme, and wood betony) will last at least 3 years in cool, dry storage. Valerian and chamomile, even when properly dried, are quite short-lived and will only remain viable for 1 or 2 years. Osha seed really only stays good for 1 year, while dried neem seed only remains viable for about 3 months.

Regardless of the shelf-life of the seeds, there are standard methods used to insure that they remain viable for as long as possible. Many gardeners keep their seeds in sealed plastic bags or jars in the refrigerator, and this works pretty well. Some seed-savers place a (commercially available) silica-based desiccant pack in with the seeds to make sure they do not take on atmospheric moisture, as keeping the seed dry is the main way to assure its longevity in storage. However, this method is useful only for small lots of seed (up to a pound or so) and is impractical for larger amounts of seed. We successfully store our seed (small lots in bags, larger lots in sacks or barrels) in a climate-controlled seed room where the temperature stays at 60° F and the humidity stays below 40%.

It is a general rule that for optimal storage of dried seeds, the sum of degrees Farenheit plus the percent relative humidity should not exceed 100. You might think that the dehumidifier would be a good option here, but actually they perform poorly at low temperature. An air conditioner, however, is extremely helpful in maintaining sufficiently cold and dry conditions for proper storage of dried seeds.

Refrigerator storage of fresh medicinal herb seeds. Certain seeds must be kept moist to stay alive, and these are best planted immediately after harvest. If for some reason this is not possible, then seeds of this sort can usually be preserved for a period of time in the refrigerator. Sometimes refrigeration in moist medium is also used to break dormancy, which can be effective in some cases (e.g. ashitaba, blue vervain, or echinacea.) When refrigerating fresh seed (e.g. spice bush, goldenseal, blue cohosh, or elderberry), it is best to mix the seed into a small amount of moist sand or coir. Use 2 parts sand or coir to 1 part seed. Mix thoroughly in a bowl or bucket, then put the seed mix in a sealed plastic bag or glass jar and refrigerate. Do not freeze, as this is likely to kill the seed.

Seed stored in this manner may last for up to a year, during which time it may begin to germinate or go bad. If the refrigerated seed begins to mold, or turn to mush, then it is certainly time to plant the remaining good seeds without delay. If the seed starts to germinate, then you can carefully plant it in a pot. Make a hole with your finger in the potting soil, dangle the root down into it, and orient the emerging green portions just below the soil surface, then fill in around the germinating seed to disallow air pockets. It will grow.

ADDENDUM B: HARVESTING & PROCESSING MEDICINAL HERBS

The energy inside plants flows with the seasons. The place the plant puts its highest energy (life force, nutrients, and medicinal compounds) will depend upon its position within the growth cycle. In the spring, it's all about the young leaves—the spring tonic. In the summer, the highest energy is in the leaves, flowers, and fruits. In the fall, the energy moves into the seeds. In the late fall, the plants die back and settle their power back into the root. Over the winter, the plant maintains its life force by using resources stored in the root. By spring, the root is somewhat exhausted, and the energy of the plant moves to the buds and newly emerging leaves. The root is now in need of a vacation. The summer leaves will photosynthesize, feeding the roots with energy from the sun. For the roots, it will be like a vacation in Bermuda. Of course there are exceptions, but most herbaceous perennials follow this scenario, so the parts of the plant that are most well-suited to harvest will vary according to the season.

Spring greens consist of leafy vegetables, like spinach and chicory, as well as the alterative and nutritive herbs, such as: chickweed, cleavers, dandelion, and plantain. Spring greens are a crucial part of the herbal spring cleanse, and indeed are a healthy ingredient to the diet at any time of the year when they might be available. The best way to utilize spring greens is direct consumption—eat them in their fresh, turgid state. Dandelion is probably the finest, filled with chlorophyll and vitamins, cleansing to the blood. This herb is a specialist in the elimination of toxins—laxative and diuretic. To make best use of dandelion, use the fresh, newly washed leaves in a salad. Throw in some chicory and chickweed for good measure. Or, you could pick the spring greens and dry them for later use in tea, tincture, or for making infused oils and salve. The best way to preserve spring greens for later use is probably to tincture them, or make a succus (an alcohol-preserved plant juice). This would be a good choice for spring herbs that are not very palatable (e.g. cleavers).

Summer flowers. Calendula is the quintessential summer flower, useful in both fresh and dried form. Harvest flowers in the late morning to early afternoon, after the dew has dried. Pick flowers on an ongoing basis, day after day, choosing only the blossoms that are in full glory (not the buds or unopened flowers, nor the flowers that are dropping petals and beginning to put energy toward making seeds).

Burdock and dandelion against staph. By the way, a combination of dandelion leaves and burdock root, when employed conscientiously as a treatment regimen, has been shown to substantially reduce or banish staphylococcus infection. This kind of therapy involves systematic fasting and avoidance of all sugar, which may prove difficult for people to accept—given these constraints, you have to want to get well. For more information on using herbs for healing, please read my book, "Making Plant Medicine."

Leafy herbs are best picked clean, that is, without a lot of dirt in the mix. Greens are best picked in the morning hours. If the leaves are to be dried, then it is definitely a good practice to wait until the dew is off the leaves, as moisture would tend to blacken them in the drying process. If the leaves are to be consumed directly, they can be picked when absolutely turgid and bejeweled by morning dew.

Dried flowers. Calendula (and a lot of other summer flowers, like: echinacea, marigold, red clover, and yarrow) can be popped off the stem, gathered in a bucket or bowl, and then laid out one flower thick on screens in a warm, dark place with positive airflow. A vegetable dehydrator works great for flowers, and they tend to dry within 1 or 2 days. Stir the drying flowers a few times within the first 12 hours, and stir again a few times as the flowers dry to completion. Store in cellophane bags, plastic bags, or sealed glass jars, cool and away from the light.

Fresh flowers can be processed immediately into tincture. A good example of this would be German chamomile, which tends to ripen its flowers within a short window of opportunity. You can go into the field and pick half a bucketful of chamomile flowers in an hour, raking them off the plant with your fingers, popping them out into the palm of your hand, and tossing them into the bucket. It smells so good, you drop into a dreamy state, half asleep on your feet, a gentle smile growing beatifically on your lips. Then you go inside and put strong alcohol on the flowers and grind them up with sharp whirring blades in a blender. Sigh. These kinds of illogical progressions are all too characteristic of modern day humans.

Dry summer leaves. Garden sage leaves are best harvested prior to flowering. The plant contains a lot of essential oil, and since oil and water don't mix, it makes sense to dry the leaf before use. Although fresh sage leaves make a good chaw and can certainly be efficaciously used in cooking, the herb is much stronger and its essence becomes more available once the leaf is dried.

Snip the stem with scissors or snips. Cut off most of the new growth, but leave a healthy node below the cut so the plant can remake the stem. This snip will yield a 6-inch leafy stem of garden sage. Now do this again. Avoid any stems that are producing flowers. You want leaves, not flowers. Bundle the stems all together, between 10 and 15 of them in a bundle. Put the snipped ends all together, with the leafy tips protruding like a broom. Use string to lasso them into a bundle (that

way you can tighten the lasso when the herb dries and shrinks) or use a rubber band (which will hold the broom together as the herb shrinks).

Stretch a string across the ceiling, above head height, in the drying shed, kitchen, or any other room where the sun does not shine on the ceiling and there is warm, positive airflow. Hang your brooms on the string. My favorite way to do this is to gently part the bundle into two leafy legs, then straddle it on the string like a cowboy trying to get over a barbed wire fence (that danged harse!), and snug it securely down onto the string by working it back and forth a little (yee ha!)

Allow the bundle to dry undisturbed for 2 or 3 days. When the outer leaves are feeling quite limp, almost desiccated, then take the bundle down and turn the outside parts in and turn the inside parts out. You might have to loosen the string to do this. The cowboy's chaps are now on the outside, his holsters between his legs; thighs out and hips in, reversed. This gives the moist, inner parts of the bundle a chance to dry evenly, and disallows darkening of the leaf or (heaven forbid) formation of mold.

After another week or more of drying, you can bring the bundle down. Now you find out why it makes sense to first dry the entire stem with leaves and then remove the leaves

from the stem. Working onto a clean, smooth table, rub the bundle between the palms of your hands. The brittle leaves will shatter off of the stems, and the stems will stay in your hand, to be set aside, composted, or used as fire starter, shish-kabobs, or giant toothpicks. If the herb doesn't all come off of the stems, then it really isn't dry enough.

Another way to remove dried leaves from stems is by rubbing the bundle on a 1/4 inch screen. This physically breaks off the leaves, which will fall through the screen and can easily be swept up from the table and put away for later use. The stems will stay on the surface of the screen. This will produce a tea cut, and is a useful size for working with dried mint. If a finer cut is desired, the leaves can be rubbed through a finer screen. This will help get rid of any small, stemmy material and will give a more consistent, fluffy medicinal herb or spice. Using graduated screens, you can even grind the herb down to a coarse powder, which is generally the grade required for tincturing. You will have to use screens of smaller and smaller mesh size, and it may take quite a bit of elbow grease.

Drying a bigger harvest. Bundling medicinal herbs for dehydration is a fine small-scale method, but if you have a whole truckload of material, then you will have to use screens. I like to make my screens out of galvanized or stainless steel 1/4 inch wire with 4-inch high frames made out of cedar. A good size is 2 feet by 3 feet. Screens of this sort can be used for drying flowers, leafy herbs, or roots. Screens are suspended horizontally in the rack, with at least 5 inches between each screen and the next. It is best to keep the rack in a warm, dry location with positive airflow. You can use a fan and a heater if ambient humidity is getting in the way of efficient dehydration. Build the rack so the screens can be heaped with herb and conveniently pulled out like drawers in a dresser. That way you can remove the screens for loading, pull them part way out to turn the herb, and again remove them when the herb is fully dry.

Dry the herbs until the stems snap. You can dump the dried herb on a clean sheet or on a table, and then stuff it in bags for storage. It is usually best to store herbs in whole form, grinding them up just prior to use. This disallows excessive oxidation, improves shelf-life, and makes superior herbal products.

Fresh summer leaves can be picked right off the plant and used—comfrey leaf for poulticing, beet leaves for juicing, elder leaves for making the light green infused oil, garden sorrel for making a delightfully toothsome cream sauce. All these herbs and many more yield their essence best in the fresh state.

Whole aerial parts may be used. For instance the potent, dream-inducing herb, passionflower (*Passiflora incarnata*), is commonly prepared by mixing the stems, leaves, and flowers. The herb is used either fresh or dried. Then again, bittersweet nightshade (*Solanum dulcamara*), an herb that is employed for treating herpes infections, is often prepared as stem only, without the leaves or fruits. Finally, the gently sedative herb, California poppy (*Eschscholzia californica*), and the powerfully alterative herb, greater celandine (*Chelidonium majus*), are both used as the entire plant—root, stem, leaf, flower, and seedpod. Both are members of the poppy family.

Dormant root harvest occurs usually in the fall, when the energy of the aerial parts of the plant has gone back down into the root. Echinacea is a good example of a root best harvested in the fall and used in the fresh state. I have noticed a tendency for bigger growers to use the root after only one year, and they swear that it makes good medicine, but the reality is that holding the plants over for a second year of growth results in a greater than 100% increase in yield.

Storing or shipping fresh roots. If the fresh roots need to be stored or shipped prior to processing, then it is best not to wash them. (They can be washed later.) Once you wash off the dirt, the root will lose its *invisible layer of protection* that keeps it from rotting. Dirty roots harbor the hope that they will find their way back into the garden soil and, because of this, they last a long time. Once you wash the root, it knows that the end is near. Most washed roots only last for a few days, a few weeks at best, before beginning to deteriorate. Harvest when the garden is not too muddy, and shake the roots free of clinging dirt.

Then, if you want to ship them off or to hold the roots for a few days (stored in a cool place like the shadehouse, a basement, or a root cellar), pack them in a washed burlap sack or in a woven plastic grain sack. Pack them dirty, alternating layers of roots and moist medium, such as coir or peat moss. Finish by drawing the top of the sack tightly down on the roots and excluding air.

Drying roots. Ashwagandha is generally harvested in the fall of the first or second growing season, the fresh roots dug from the field, washed, chopped, and dried. If one is drying roots of any kind, it is best to chop them while they are fresh and soft, because they can be very slow to dry and difficult to grind up if dried in the whole form. Probably the epitome of this would be the American wild yam, which can be snipped with difficulty in the fresh state, but once dried transforms into the hardest substance known to herbalist.

If I were hanging by an herb from a cliff over a vast canyon and had to rely on that herb not to break, lest I go plunging to certain death far below, plummeting down and landing with a thump amidst bright ribands of flowing water reflecting a noontide sun like diamond awareness, the sculpted rock outcroppings, red and yellow, having been worn by the leathern feet of countless generations of native people, washing their hair, tossing nets, singing and laughing below, the noisy hubbub of humanity reaching my whistling ears and dissolving in thin air as I plunge into this bright, eternal OM—then I would choose wild yam. It's the kind of root you can stake your life on.